MASTHEAD

EDITORS	M.Bartley Seigel Roxane Gay
ASSOCIATE EDITOR	Brad Green
ASSISTANT EDITORS	Abby Koski Jason Sommer
COVER ARTIST	Elena Duff
COVER DESIGNER	Jeff Kuure

READERS

Mairead Case
Sara Crowley
Court Merrigan
Matthew Robinson
Diana Salier
Eric Shonkwiler
Joe Stracci
Robb Todd
Hedy Zimra

Cecil Giscombe
Bob Hicok
Taylor Mali
Michael Martone
Daniel Nester
Amber Tamblyn
Keith Taylor
Kette Thomas
Deb Olin Unferth

ADVISORY BOARD

www.pankmagazine.com

Founded in 2006, the nonprofit literary arts collective [PANK] —PANK Magazine, pankmagazine.com, the Little Book Series, and the Invasion Readings — fosters access to emerging and experimental poetry and prose, publishing the brightest and most promising writers for the most adventurous readers. To the end of the road, up country, a far shore, the edge of things, to a place of amalgamation and unplumbed depths, where the known is made and unmade, and where unimagined futures are born, a place inhabited by contradictions, a place of quirk and startling anomaly, [PANK], no soft pink hands allowed. Direct all correspondence to [PANK], 305 Walker Center, 1400 Townsend Dr., Houghton, Michigan 49931, or email awesome@pankmagazine.com. Online issues, subscription and donation information, and submission guidelines are available at www.pankmagazine.com.
ISSN: 1935-7133. Copyright © [PANK].

CONTENTS

RETURNS

REBECCA MORGAN FRANK

There it was, like a paper valentine, a cookie-cutter
slab of beating meat, somebody's supper, a matter
that gathers grease at the top of the can. The sitting on the shelf,
the past A-grade, the everyday housemaid to my daily tasks.
The not-to-be-spoken device, a regular older ticker, tocking
out of line, now out of time. A lump that had misplaced the shadows
standing in the kitchen making supper, shaping warmth
next to me in the bed. It had followed me around like a mangy
dog looking for scraps, had stood out on the corner and begged.
Had handed out flowers. Had received them. Had gone
down cobbled alleys and hiked up to an arch of rocks
to the stars. Had died, been resuscitated, sat by the hospital bed,
checked itself in for rehab. Had given up, gone on welfare,
rented itself out for rooms. Been advertised on sale. Set out
for China. Dreamt of Paris. Been given a pink slip and a wave.
Been mimeographed, deleted, returned with postage due.

INSTALLATION IN CITY: INTERSECTIONS OF BODIES

REBECCA MORGAN FRANK

Gray knots of limbs, legs wrapped through crooks,
a chain link gang of bodies boring its way through
the street. No weight supports its own. The hands
walk concrete, knees scrape, a head hovers over
the curb: traffic bends and boldens around it, not
stopped but startled out of symmetry. Hands wave
from the mass of bodies, the bulk of automobiles,
and then the beast unfurls, flings
                              a fragile frame out in leaps of grass,
a round ass to the grate shadowed by a truck, three
tall men in tights unravel, unrolling up to the skyscraper roofs,
lost in sight to the endless supply of tiny bodies spinning
out, out into the gaps between the cars, dervishes
unwrapping capes like wings and the intersection flies–
the cars kill their engines. The city stops.

I AM TURNING INTO MY FATHER

SARAH TOURJEE

I am turning into my father. It began gradually. My joints began to ache in the rain, my brow furrowed into a long canal. One night I stood on the porch for a long time just staring into the woods. I am having conversations with the radio now, I ask it how the hell it can be on the air and still be so stupid. I rake the leaves into small piles all around the yard. My hair is turning gray, and the names of all the trees have settled behind my eyes. I talk to my uncle for long stretches of time as though he's my brother. "Are you drinking again, Rick?" he says to me, but my father's name is Rick and I'm twelve. "Fuck off, Darren," I say easily.

My mother mistakes me for him sometimes, too. "I'm leaving," she says to me. "I haven't been in love with you in a long time."

"I'm your son," I say.

"I know that," she says, but I suspect she is lying. Perhaps she would rather I think she was once in love with me— her son—but isn't anymore, rather than the truth: that my mother is leaving.

When I go to school everyone stares at me. My teacher talks to me and calls me Rick. "My name is not Rick," I say and she laughs and touches her hair. All the while I try to remember if she is Mrs. or Miss. I take off my glasses and wipe them with my shirt. I don't even wear glasses. *My wife is leaving me*, I think. I panic. The wife I am thinking of is not my wife but my mother. I am concerned that this transformation is occurring not just physically, but mentally. The next step is that I will remember certain intimacies and conceptions in vivid detail with a sigh of sadness and longing. This is too much.

My eyes are getting dark, my nose bigger, my smell strange. I stand on the porch and try to think about things that only I would think about. Thoughts my father would never think. Things that split and regrow: worms, water, fingers when stored in milk, starfish. I trace the scar along my knuckle and think about what it felt like to lose a finger. I know my father could not know how that feels, he could not think these specific thoughts. I doubt that he even remembers it happening. If I can think about it, then I know I am me.

I like to fell trees. That's something my father always says about me. I like the rhythm of the cutting, and I feel strong. It's good that we have a wood stove, or else my parents probably would not have let me cut down all those trees in the woods behind our house. It's good to fell a tree, especially when you cannot fell much else. But, if you are only one person using a two person saw, you must take special care not to cut yourself. You could cut off a whole finger, which is what I did. It must have hurt, but mainly I just remember seeing a piece of myself that was not a part of me anymore. I remember thinking, when I picked it up, *My fingernails are sort of strange, sort of flat.*

I had never thought that before. I thought this must be what other people think when they have the chance to see my fingernails. It's the sort of thing you can only see about yourself when you are not yourself. I didn't know what kind of tree it was. I only got part way through the trunk before it happened, and after that I didn't feel like felling trees.

Now I know that tree is a white pine. It's my father who knows the names of trees. When I look in the mirror I see dark pointy hairs sticking out of my nostrils. I see patches of hair on my chest, and clusters of protruding moles. When I look in the mirror, I know things. I know I like a glass or two of scotch at night. I know where I went those nights I didn't come home. I know what it looked like when I was born, and when I slept in my crib, and how my eyelids fluttered like I was already thinking of things even then. And I know the name of my wife's lover. My mother's lover.

■

Uncle Darren comes by and says he's glad I'm home, that he wants to talk to me. "I'm sorry about what I said on the phone," I say, afraid he'll tell my father, but he looks surprised.

"Oh, so am I."

"I saw you," I say.

"I know that," he says. My face gets hot and I look out off the porch and into the woods.

"Look I'm sorry about all that," he says. "It shouldn't have happened, not like that. But Susan and I – we've been talking."

"Yes, I know," I say, and then I do.

"We both tried to forget about it, really. But fuck, can you honestly tell me you've been happy? It's been bad for a while between you two. Nothing to do with me really. I mean think about Craig."

"*I'm* Craig." I say.

■

That day, I brought the finger home and my mother held me and placed it in a small glass of milk until the doctor laced a needle through its mangled edges forcing it to reclaim its hand.

I could not stop wondering, did my finger resent this? I thought of a worm cut in half, sealing its wounds and remaining as two worms. If my finger found itself suddenly with life of its own in a pool of milk, what had it thought then when it could think for itself? I held it in front of my eyes, and bent it, curled it at the knuckle. As it healed, I watched the scar around the base stretch, I watched the skin change color until it was mine again. I half expected the finger to resist my command to bend, but of course it did not resist. No one has ever sewn a worm back together and sent the life of the second worm back to wherever it had come from. This is what happened to my finger though, and I couldn't stop thinking about it. But when I think about it now, it does not feel like my story. These do not sound like my thoughts.

"Don't you even want to discuss the fact that I'm leaving you?" My mother corners me at the breakfast table.

"I will miss you," I say. I don't know if these are my father's words or mine. I don't know which of us she's talking to.

"You can't just say that at the end. I needed to know it from the beginning."

"I'm your son," I say.

"I know that," she says, with a pause.

Is this scar on my finger the last physical trace of me on my own body, or is it the first trace of me on his? What happens to the one of us who is left? And why didn't he ever say he'd miss her?

■

Truth be told, I knew about the affair before my mother confessed. I was out felling trees and my wife and Darren were out felling each other. I don't mean to be crude, I mean to be quiet but it's difficult. I stood on the porch watching Craig struggling with a two person saw, which I understood. I thought I should help him, but then he stopped and seemed to peer into the woods. From the porch my father had a better view than I of the mixture of arms and legs seeming to grow up from the leaves—the limbs of my brother and my wife. My wife is very beautiful, and my father is not, and that much I understood. I knew that my son could not understand, and then I heard a yell and I saw the blood, and my father ran down to me, leaning on the tree I had been attempting to fell. And there was the finger, which I picked up while my wife held onto Craig, saying, "You're all right, sweetie, you're all right," and covering my face in her sweater so I wouldn't see the blood and my lonely knuckle, or my uncle just standing there like a goddamn tree. In the house my father gave the finger to my mother to put in a cup of milk, because I guess I knew that Craig would need this memory of his mother saving this lost piece. So I gave it to her.

■

"Is this my life?" my father asks me. He stands in front of me, looks me up and down. "What an idiot. There are things you could have done better," he says and peers deep into my eyes. "But you were always waiting."

"What did I do wrong?" I say. "Waiting for what?"

"For conversations to be had in your sleep, for the end of the bottle, for the second wind—the rally. She stopped waiting. You can't blame her for that." I know what he means. He's talking to me like I'm a mirror in the bathroom. I'm talking to myself in a mirror in the bathroom.

I see my mother's reflection behind me. "I didn't want to hurt you," she says, "but I haven't been happy."

"I haven't been happy either," I say, "but I would like you to be."

"I know that," she says.

"You should talk to him," I say.

She nods. "Have you seen him?" she says, and looks around.

ELECTROCUTION, KESSLER FARM, 1988

BRANDON COURTNEY

Working your tongue into words, anointing the wound small
        as a keyhole, you tried to explain the lave of electrocution:

your first death, ten years before the real one, your body ironed
        flat on the barn wood floor; tincture of piss darkening the denim

around your zipper, wires tangled like kudzu vines, spilling
        from the fuse box. Electricity to stop your heart, two-hundred

volts sent you reeling—the light that found its way from your body
        through an imperfect path—piercing earth like a railroad spike.

The bright arc, blue as lightning strike, punched through fabric;
        flesh of your right elbow, after you scraped the copper busbar

of the switchboard with your wedding ring. In the hospital,
        the cotton of anesthesia burned off, you awoke to a surgeon

removing the gold band from your finger with bolt cutters.
        Silent, you watched him circle the asterisk burns, trace the current's

path from humerus to heart with a grease pencil, snaking
        black ink across your bare chest like the lines of a creek map.

Think of fire, the way it cuts into hardwood like a planer
        blade, your fingernail darkened like a room filling with smoke.

Think of the heat it takes to bear diamonds, the geode of coins
        the surgeon pulled from your breast pocket: loose change

fused together, somehow brighter than before.

BAYEUX, NORMANDY, JUNE

CAITLIN HORROCKS

It was a roadside motel exactly like any other roadside motel, and we could pretend that was a cultural experience, too, this discovery of sameness. Maybe it was. The view from our window was of a parking lot, another motel, an animal hospital with an oval wooden paddock. "Maybe we'll get to see some horses," I said. We were tourists, and *seeing*—novelties, differences, beautiful things or just very old ones—was what we were there to do.

We walked along the road towards dinner, into the narrow stony streets of the town. We got lost, got un-lost. I repeated myself four times at the restaurant before the waiter understood me. The food was not quite what we thought we were ordering. We walked home past a church four times older than our nation.

The next morning we would walk along a thousand-year-old tapestry, the reason we'd come to this town, this particular town. The embroidery would tell a war story: horses and knights, ships and soldiers, the Normans arriving in Britain. The blood spilled would be orange, because there was no red dye then, *red* an invention that came later, after swords and sails, after conquest, after language. We spilled blood for centuries without any way to remember it beyond our bodies, our voices, our words. The tapestry would end in ragged threads, the story unresolved, the final triumph missing. There would be no label to explain this mystery. The audioguide would be swift and smug. We would be pushed by the people behind us out of the dim tapestry room, blinking in the sudden light of the gift shop, and the day after that we would fly back to America.

But that night we sat at the motel window, staring at the parking lot. There were no horses. We watched a cat on a neighboring windowsill bat optimistically at sparrows. We didn't understand the television; we were tired of our books. It felt late in the trip for more wine out of plastic motel cups. We'd already had too much wine, in other towns, other restaurants, other rooms. The evening was late, the streetlights buzzing into bloom. The cat, framed by white curtains, crept all the way out onto the second-story windowsill. Still, it could not catch the birds. But still, it did not fall.

We watched the windowless animal hospital, the front doors locked and dark. A young couple emerged from a side door. They walked close, but not hand in hand, or arm in arm. They could have been siblings, or lovers, or just friends. There was no way of knowing. There is still no way of knowing who they were.

"Their dog just died," Todd invented, and I rolled my eyes. The man and woman walked silently across the parking lot. Nearly to their car, she bent her head and began to sob. "Oh, shit," Todd said. "Their dog *did* die."

Or cat, or guinea pig, or horse. But because we like dogs more than other animals, that was the shape of her grief, wordless and instantly translated. Her body crumpled, and the man put his arms around her. How often had this happened? How many people had glanced out of this hotel onto someone else's misery? I thought I should look away. I did not think about trying to comfort her. We sat in the dark. They couldn't have seen us, two heads in a window, the stitched outlines of travelers, voyeurs. *Voyeurs*—a French word, borrowed. How did we not have one of our own? How would we have managed without it? What might I have called myself, in some other language?

But they never looked up. They were their own world. Wordless, their bodies, their voices. Out the window they held each other and their grief was as loud as the highway, the pavement and green hills. Louder than a town, a church, a thousand-year-old war. As deafening as stars, as endless as sky. The sound of her sobbing is the arc of the earth, invisible but unbroken.

THE SPA FOR GRIEF

CATHERINE OWEN

This—all that's left when the water is burned off—
two brimming handfuls of bone, here &

there a bit of a tooth, a link of his silver chain not ground
down by the cremulator. I am sorry to have to tell you this.

She is rubbing oil into my feet and her voice too is unguent,
slowly soothing me into silence, as if these facts don't matter

now, not here, and she is right, I think, though it is hard
not to tell her of the chill cringe of dead flesh

and how I lifted his shirt fast to see where they'd stitched,
stroking the coarse indifferent sutures of autopsy like braille

and how around his eyes pooled the blue & gray abrasions of fluid,
bloomings from his four long days of death.

Now I have to pay to be touched, a woman's hands holding
the feet he loved, and not loving them, not offering his gifts,

but still somehow massaging each digit into a kind of feeling,
then, painting the nails red, as if with joy.

YELLOW

CRISTIN O'KEEFE APTOWICZ

is the happiest pair of shoes I know.
It's a bedroom I want to live in one day,
the ceramic puma crouching in the living
room of my childhood best friend, whose
family I now suspect were in the mafia.

Yellow was the ugliest car, was my snowsuit,
was the natural color of my teeth, according
to my matter-of-fact dentist. Yellow is pencils,
long and short, sharpened or blunt. All of them.
Yellow is a flower everyone else called a weed.

Yellow is slur, is an insult, flung to mean Other,
to mean cowardly or foreign. Yellow means
banana, or lemon, or custard, or mustard,
or butter. Yellow means fat, or gristle. Yellow
means jaundice, or bad kidneys, or both.

No one ever made The Yellow Album. Knights
don't ride in on shining yellow horse. Even hair
doesn't want to be called it; *Blonde, not Yellow*
my kindergarten teacher would correct me.
Tell that to my crayon I wanted to say.

Yellow is primary, is just as important as red or blue.
Yellow isn't kids stuff. It isn't the official color
of gender neutral. It isn't always happy all the time.
The sun is yellow; it burns constantly. Yellow doesn't
need you. You are the one that needs Yellow.

MY TINY GOD

CRISTIN O'KEEFE APTOWICZ

likes balance. He has me step in dog shit today
so I might catch an express train next week. He likes
how happy I am to earn it. How suffering to me is
like loading a gift card in karma's outlet mall.

My Tiny God knows I like established paths, following
dotted lines to my destination. My Tiny God thinks
no one learns anything that way, turns off the headlights
when we're still racing down a road.

Still, My Tiny God is the one I pray to on a rainy tarmac,
in the waiting room, on the other end of a static-filled line.
My Tiny God doesn't always takes my calls. I don't know
if he listens to my voicemails. Sometimes he goes missing.

I remind myself he doesn't have to watch over me all the time.
He doesn't need to carry his scale everywhere. He is allowed
to gets bored. He doesn't have to watch me write for me to know
that he likes it when I've written, to see the paper pile up.

These days, My Tiny God clocks in every morning. Coffee,
our favorite miracle. Work, our favorite song. Faith, our lucky number.
He pours sunlight on me like syrup, fluffs every bright cloud,
smacks the birds from the trees just so I can watch them scatter.

AFTER READING YOUR POEM ABOUT HAWAII

CRISTIN O'KEEFE APTOWICZ

I once wrote a poem about how you can
make a phone stop ringing. It's true.
You can make that call just not happen.
Or you can make it happen.

Ring ring, I tell my friend who says
he wants to his ex-lover to stop calling,
but he can't help but conjure her rings.
He just wants to make sure she gets it,

he says, he just want to make sure that
everyone is on the same page. *That's not
important,* I tell him. *What's important is
that the phone needs to stop ringing.*

You need to agree to let each other go,
and then you need to let each other go.

Poems are phone calls you can eavesdrop on.
When you are a poet, poems are everywhere.
I still read your poetry. Sometimes I think
I still see me in there.

But other times I know that's not the truth.
The truth is that we both know where we are,
and it's not next to each other anymore.
So what am I to make of this poem?

Where you are the *you* I am speaking to,
when in real life we are not speaking at all.
Ring ring, my brain says. Or maybe, it can
just be my poem waving to your poem.

Aloha is a word that means *hello* and *goodbye*.
Aloha is also a word that means *peace*.

THE DMZ

DENNIS JAMES SWEENEY

There are fifty people signed up for the tour of the Demilitarized Zone. Commonly abbreviated as DMZ. One of them sits in the loft of a restaurant and bar with the name Liberty. A giant stencil of Bob Marley on the yellow wall. On the stereo you have Elvis. You have the Beach Boys. You have James Brown. Hot damn.

The member of the tour stares at the table he sits Indian style before. It was crispy noodles. Now it is nothing. It may be he is tired from all the buses. It may be he is gathering his thoughts. Surely there is an excuse for his silence when below a quartet of Australians shoots pool for beer. Narrates every shot. Is irrepressibly happy. He could be French. He could be Australian. He could be German or English. You can't tell from looking at him.

When a couple walks up the stairs to the otherwise empty loft he looks at them and smiles in a tight-lipped way. Then he looks back down at the table.

This is the night before the tour. Johnny Cash comes on. He hears a train a-comin'.

In the morning he stares the same way out the window of the bus. The front window with burgundy plastic chairs between him and it. The side window crusted with white ghosts of water drops.

He also puts his elbow on the arm rest. His cheek on his hand. His eyes are closed. God knows if he sleeps.

In the tunnels north of the 17th parallel he is a normal person. He is the one who sits in the cubbies labeled family room and looks at the nearby walls. Which gets mud on his ass. Otherwise he is a normal person bending below the arch of rock. In a single-file line neither hell-bound nor heaven.

At lunch he can be seen talking to an English person who looks like an Indian. Eating fried rice with vegetable and egg. Gesturing even. Distracted at the end of every speech act by the documentary on the war on the mounted TV on the wall. Every head drifts there.

To look at the Rockpile he gets out on the side of the highway like everyone else. His hands in his pockets like everyone else. The gusts of cold air mingling the smokers' breath with the non-. Whisking it away before the union matters. Past the gap in the jungle in back of the guardrail. The green that only the Viet Cong know.

They find him at Khe Sanh crouched in the overgrown bunker with his back against the sandbags. Between his back and the sandbags a piece of metal with regular can-sized holes in it. Held into place by two metal beams hammered into the dirt. Across from two metal pipes half-filled with water pointing upright from the floor.

The English Indian asks what he is doing and he covers his ears with his fingers and lowers his head to his knees. The English Indian says the bus is waiting for him so let's go and he covers his ears and lowers his head again. He beckons frantically with his hand. For the English Indian to come next to him and squat.

The English Indian leaves. He returns with the tour guide. With his sharp Vietnamese cheek bones. He assesses the person braced against the bunker with the grassy bomb crater outside and the barbed wire woven wings and propeller past that. This crouching figure.

Who looks sideways out of the crook of his arms. And stands up. And raises his arms in the air. And his knuckles hit the corrugated steel of the ceiling.

"I am an American!" he says. "I am an American!" he says. And once more, he says: "I am an American!"

And he falls to his knees and then to his face in the clay of the bunker floor. Pelted miraculously by a bird that flew through the narrow shooting window.

The bird lies next to his head. Stunned. Ten seconds. It flickers a wing. Then rises to its spindly feet.

It flaps. Hops. Flaps and hops again. It flies away through the bunker door.

Out of which the two men look. Over the motionless person. To the fog that whispers by the dirt track runway. By the behemoth cargo airplane anchored permanently there. Its tail. Its wing. The offhangs of its fuselage. Appearing and disappearing in the rolling white.

PREPARING TO LAUNCH

ELIZABETH CANTWELL

the rescue mission   we
have seen the hammering in the
(wind)pipes   we have grown attached
to firearms   the body is itself
combustible at certain angles   did you know,
Sophia, how the journey out
would trick your cells into believing
time had stopped   was that the reason
you wanted to go   visions of
millions of Sophia cells arrested
in their daily orbits through your
limbs danced in your head   did you also
know how quickly bodies learn
to recognize relativistic tricks
and override them   silly girl
stasis is for the dead

who is as silver as the polished ring
is ready for her traction   contraction
of the abs   absolute silence in
the halls   holistic kiss of meta-
morphosis   you won't even be asked
to move a muscle   when the time comes
they'll do all the moving
for you

CONTACT

ELIZABETH CANTWELL

the sound of a buzzard   landing
next to your hands   on the mirror

if you look up   you will see
first your face and then   your
other face

WE CALLED IT THE YEAR OF BIRTHING

for Micah Rajan George and his unbreakable parents

EUGENIA LEIGH

God handed me a trash bag bloated with feathers. *Turn this*
into a bird, he said. He threw me a bowl of nails. *And make with this,*
a new father. God gave some people
whole birds. Readymade fathers with no loose bolts.
The rest of us received crude nests. Used mothers.

I banged the nails into two planks of wood
and marched around a church screaming, *Father, father*
until friends appeared, hammering
the scraps they were given to make something of themselves.

When beaten hard enough, some people scamper into corners
sordid with similar beaten people. Others of us—
the stubborn, unbreakable humans—weld our wounds
to form tools. Then we spend our days
mending bent humans or wiping the humans
mired by all the wrong fingerprints.

The morning the first baby was born in our circle of friends,
we hovered over this child who, unlike us,
was born whole. *You were given a good mother*, we said. *A good father.*
Each one of us prayed.   We scrubbed our soiled hands
before we held his swaddled body.

THE JAR PARTY

EUGENIA LEIGH

They gravitate to my scars. Awkward
humans gasping, *Yours matches mine—*
Then with biblical celebrity, cult camaraderie,
Your mom was almost— My mom also—

We gush and hug, exchange numbers
to arrange for our mothers to meet—as though
women gather for this sort of thing—
to crochet scars over cocktails.

I collect fractured humans and store them
in a bell jar for moments

I want *normal*. Sometimes,

I shrink myself to join the jar party.
We behave like nine thousand blind people
in a room with no door—every one of us
shouting   for an exit.

POLITICS, 2004

HILARY JACQMIN

For Halloween that year, we went as Bill
and Hill, pre-second term, pre-Monica.
I pushed my bangs back with a braided headband

and disinterred my pinstriped interview suit
from the chifferobe, where it lay smothered
in clear plastic. I was too tall—and too brunette—

to play my near-namesake, Hillary, but you were bluff
and Clintonesque in navy and a Windsor knot,
glad-handing the guests, your sandy curls streaked white

with Gold Bond, then teased into a pompadour,
your blue eyes pilot lights. When midnight struck,
I couldn't wait for everyone to leave:

the pair of Russian cosmonauts twined
together on the La-Z-Boy; three frat
guys dressed as Uncle Sam; a hanging chad.

I'd been with you—split cherry pancake breakfasts
at the Roosevelt, canvassed your roommate, your cat—
since Labor Day, two Indian summer months

evaporated into fall. By the time
John Kerry gave his glum concession speech
(we wept in Video American),

I'd scored a doctor's scrip for birth control
and booked a suite in Washington, D.C.—
but all that was still to come. That Halloween,

we swayed to "Jesus of Suburbia"
beneath looped yards of bunting, your blazered left
arm wrapped around my waist, a whiskey-breathing

one-night-only politico and his wannabe
First Lady, suntan pantyhose run through,
just some small-town power couple, wired with hope.

TO ...AND

JAMES MAY

...ind the bed in the guestroom
...y (you must have stayed there
...marriage), I found
..., spackled
...of its scent. Which,
...robably of bourbon
...ps. And yesterday,
...ers to the jays,
...me ripping the English ivy from the lawn.
...n you caused her.
...gh, we cursed you for doing nothing
about the ivy when years ago you told her
you were going to do something about the ivy.
You've become, almost, a god,
some genius loci of neglect, indifference, and mistakes.
Yet I know somewhere someone might be thinking the same about me.
The woman I moved to Houston with, married now
to the second bassoonist in the symphony,
no doubt recites my faults. And he has promised himself and her,
that he will be better than me. And he is.
They probably even have jokes where my secrets—
once promised as secrets—wait faithfully at the punch line.
Or if they're past that, it's because they bonded over talks
about how I hurt her, talked her into moving to the armpit of Texas
only to leave her three months later.
Which isn't true, exactly. But. I scrub the wall.
The water softens this crust and revives for a moment
your bile, its eye-watering stench.

THE MISTS

JEREMY BAUER

Johnny cooked the mists, clouds of deep
chuckles that stayed up all night huffing gold
spray paint and spending Johnny's money
on butterfly knives and glocks. Johnny went near wolf dog,
turned skittery manimal always slinking to the shed
behind the double wide his mother left him. He'd throw
parties where his new shriveled friends brought orange-
haired weed and weird pornos with names like *EXXXTREME
BUTTS 9* and sat giggling like elves over the outrageous
sex. Johnny's eyes turned black stagnant ponds
where the worst things bred. The mists were swelling, growing
with each assembly-line style cook Johnny performed.
What a Ford, what praise he deserved for ensuring
the Midwest glowed—a beacon of efficiency. The mists
took trophy antlers and gored the drywall, threw nail
bombs at cats that wandered into Johnny's yard.
The mists distracted people with pussy jokes
while they swirled around their teeth eating rust spots
into their smiles. Johnny used to have a motorcycle
and a factory job. Johnny used to have wormholes
in his chest, could transport you to other worlds
by taking his shirt off and holding you close. One night
the mists disappeared into the shed with a blowtorch.
Johnny ran from the cat-piss pyre through the hayfield
to the woods behind the park. He went rabbit, hid
in the moist ground. Johnny's body was vibrating
outside of time and bursting small pockets of space.
Johnny remembered welding brake pedals
and his mother's funeral. He pulled at his skin
but it only came off near the sores. He thought,
when you start shitting in the woods, you can
never return from the world of animals.

THE WOMAN NEXT DOOR

KATHRYN HOUGHTON

I don't leave the house, except for Sundays, of course, but church is God's house, so it doesn't count as getting away. Father told the school he decided to homeschool me, and even though there were only three weeks until the end of the year, no one in the office raised question or complaint. They are used to things like this from my family, and from the others who attended my church's school through eighth grade. Even if my parents have never pulled me out of school before, they call each semester to exempt me from health class, to make sure the English teacher assigns me appropriate books for class assignments, to demand the school stop teaching evolution, to complain when the school says they won't.

It's only partly a lie that I am being taught at home. Every few days Father gives me Bible verses to read, never mind that summer vacation started weeks ago. Once, Mother gave me a list of vocabulary words from Shakespeare. I learned the entire list in an afternoon, copying the definitions carefully from a twenty-year-old dictionary, but then Father found out and took the list away from me. The Bible, he says, read the Bible until you learn. Some days, when Father is at work, I look through the notes I took during history and algebra and even biology, but I have to hide them away again before he gets home. When he is home, I spend most of my time sitting in front of my bedroom window, looking out toward the house next door. The woman who lives there spends hours outside, sweeping. She goes over the same areas again and again, beating her broom against the pavement in uneven patterns, until something satisfies her. Then she will sit in the faded yellow lawn chair she's set up just outside her door. She will sit for a few moments, but then, when she looks around and sees the broom propped up against the doorjamb, she will begin again. I watch her during the day, and at night I can hear her. It keeps me awake.

■

Tonight is our church's annual purity ball. Father is taking my sister instead of me. Elizabeth is only eight, but she's getting all dressed up, complete with her first ever pair of heels. They're shiny white, half an inch tall. Mother bought them special for the occasion even though I offered one of my old pairs. I know Elizabeth prefers new things to the hand-me-downs she usually gets, but I was trying to be supportive, to show how I accept being displaced.

Father is dressed up too, in the same suit he wears every year, used only for the ball and the occasional wedding or funeral. Together, he and my sister will head downtown to the banquet center, a big fancy building with color changing lights and fish tanks lining the hallways. The chairs will be comfortable, the food will be good, and I know all of this because just two months back, I was there for prom with Allen from choir. Just two months ago it was me wearing the high heels, a shawl wrapped demurely about my shoulders, posing for pictures at the bottom of the stairs, smiling, while Elizabeth looked on.

Now I am disgraced. That's the word everyone keeps using: disgraced. That's what Father says, my pastor. They say I am not allowed to go to the ball this year. They say I need to stay home and "experience the acute pain of separation." I feel no pain—not from the ball, anyway—but I keep this to myself.

Another thing forbidden to me is youth group, which I used to attend twice a week. That's fine, in a way. The boys there stare at me when they think I'm not looking and sometimes when they know I am. They whisper things when Pastor Lewis, our youth group leader, is out of earshot, say things about my body I've been taught no Christian boy ever says. Before the Easter service, someone grabbed me from behind, but when I turned around, body rigid, a whole group of them stood there, grinning at me. I told one of the other girls in the group, but she only wanted to know what it felt like.

Mother says Father should ignore our pastor and take both me and Elizabeth this year. She said I need the ball now more than ever. Father looked at her and said, "Marie," in that stern voice he uses when someone has especially disappointed him, the voice I've heard so much lately.

"Why can't she go?" Elizabeth asked, looking up from where she sat, next to me.

Mother looked from me to Father and back again. I pushed my mashed potatoes into a mound on the side of my plate.

"Why?" Elizabeth asked again.

"She doesn't want to go," Mother said.

"Dammit Marie!" Father slammed his fist into the table, fork still clutched in his hand. Mother flinched, and even Elizabeth, who had been watching the rest of us closely, as if looking for some clue, turned away.

"She's not allowed," he said. "She broke her vow. She's not pure." Then, as if this hadn't been enough, as if Elizabeth still might not understand what was going on: "She had sex. She's lucky we don't kick her out."

Mother pushed back her chair and left the room.

I said an extra prayer for her that night as I lay in bed listening to my parents' raised voices. I asked God to give her strength, to be a good wife, but somewhere even further inside the place from which I prayed, I wanted her to take that strength for herself. I prayed for my father, though that should have come first. I prayed for Elizabeth, but I no longer knew what to ask for her. Last, I prayed for myself, because my role is to be patient, to serve, not to question, and even if I didn't voice any, I knew God could see the hundreds of questions held in my heart.

■

I met Allen in Chorale, the highest and most prestigious choir at our school. It's much more distinguished than the regular choir even students with no prior musical background can join. Chorale means auditions, harder music, longer rehearsals. It was the talk of the school for a week when I got in, the only sophomore in memory to do so, though Mr. Bowermann told me later that a freshman got in the second year he taught. "Voice like an angel," he said, and I like to think he meant me too.

No one talked about my talent, how I had gotten perfect scores at the state competition four years straight. The nicest rumor that circulated the school was that I must have done a lot of sucking up during freshman year. The rest of what was said made me blush. "I'd put her in the front row, too," I overheard one boy saying. "And just think, she's only a sophomore." He saw me then, looked me up and down real slow, smiling like we were sharing a private joke, like I had something to do with the shape of my body. That night I spent an hour looking through old photo albums, comparing myself at age eight to the way Elizabeth looked now, trying to decide if she would be the same as me, the same as our mother—thinking that maybe if I caught it now, I could save her.

"Your body is a gift given to you by God," Mother said after my series of careful questions later that night. "It's His test, your opportunity to show that you are good and pure, even if you have been given…" she trailed off, her eyes resting momentarily on my chest then darting away as a faint blush rose in her cheeks. I knew she wouldn't say the word, that she thought it was evil and dirty. But that's not how it had sounded when Allen said, later, that mine were beautiful. That wasn't the phrasing he used, and I had blushed the same as my mother, but coming from him, it hadn't sounded quite so wrong.

"You are for your husband," Father said, looking up from his newspaper to give Mother a look that warned she had gone too far. "That's all you need to worry about."

■

Next door, the woman sometimes sweeps for hours into the night, working her way down her front walk, to the driveway and then sidewalk. Sometimes she will sweep the road, pushing the leaves around in the gutter. She never collects any of it, never pushes it into a dustbin or trash bag of any sort. I pray for windy nights so that the rustle of leaves and straw against pavement sounds natural, but when the wind comes, I feel guilty thinking about her out in the cold, alone, watching her careful piles unmake themselves before her eyes, and it's as if, by invoking God, I've wished this upon her.

Other nights, still nights, when it seems as if the world might be only what I can see from my bedroom window, I pretend I hear a rhythm in her movements and, matching it perfectly, sing hymns into my pillow until I finally fall asleep.

∎

It's only the second year our church has hosted its own purity ball here in town, but this year would have been my sixth ball. Before, Father and I used to drive to one held by a sister church nearly three hours away. We would make a trip of it, just the two of us. We'd drive up Friday night, spend two nights in a hotel suite with a big bed and, once, a Jacuzzi tub that Father let me try while he flipped through the channels on the television in the other room. I loved that time together, so close, like fathers and daughters should be. He would listen to me talk about school as we ate room service, he sitting in the corner armchair while I sat on the bed. Later, when competing feelings of embarrassment at still being his little girl began to creep in alongside my delight at being so special to him, I told myself that any good girl would want such a relationship. The discomfort was God's way of testing my devotion to my father, to see if my love for him, my obedience to him, would overrule any questions or doubts. Father loved me, protected me. There was nothing to be ashamed of. Elizabeth would have given anything to be in my place.

Father was supposed to spend this kind of time with me throughout the year—me and Elizabeth—but the summer purity ball was the only time he seemed to get around to it. Most nights he didn't even remember to say goodnight. Mother said he was too busy and tired from work. He could have spent the evenings with me, at least some of them, but instead he patrolled the sidewalks of the local college, passing out pamphlets and trying to save the poor students from their sins. "You have to share him," Mother told me and Elizabeth over yet another dinner where his place sat empty. "You are blessed to already be saved, to have such a strong spiritual leader under this roof. But there are many people who still haven't seen The Way, who still don't know how to behave."

Father never took Elizabeth out either, not to dinner, not even to a movie with her friends on her birthday, and never to the ball. *Later*, he always told her, *when you're older*. Two years ago, whatever he said to her made her cry. It was Thursday, the night before we were to leave for our weekend together, and after he'd slammed his bedroom door shut behind him, muttering to himself, I went to Elizabeth's room and climbed into bed with her, pulling her curled body close to mine. The evening still held most of the day's warmth, her window open to catch a nonexistent breeze, but she pulled away. I pretended I couldn't tell she was crying.

I didn't ask what he'd said to her; I could imagine enough. But, mostly, I didn't want my sister to hear in my voice how relieved I was to still be his favorite. I wanted him to love her, but not on the little time that was reserved for me. After half an hour or so, her breathing slowed into a steady cadence, and I kissed her hair then returned to my own bed.

∎

Tonight, as Elizabeth models her pale pink dress, she keeps looking over her shoulder at me. Father is making her practice walking in her high heels, making her walk in circles around the living room and up and down the stairs. I remember how that felt, teetering on the narrow heels, holding my arms out slightly to the sides. Except with me, Father nodded occasionally, and his silence then was the same as praise.

"Can't have that tonight," he says as Elizabeth trips over the hem of her dress on the bottom stair. "Try it again," For a minute I want to smile, smug in the thought that I did this thing better than my sister.

"I won't fall," Elizabeth says, and her eyes grow wide as she looks at him. She looks so young, and I remember that my sister is younger now than I was when I attended my first ball, that I had to have struggled just as much with the heels. We have to stick together, she and I, and I'll do my part. I give her an encouraging smile, but she all her attention is on Father and she doesn't notice.

Elizabeth doesn't start moving again until he waves a prompting hand toward her.

"There aren't any stairs at the banquet center," I say.

Elizabeth looks at me questioningly, and when I nod, the tension leaves her shoulders.

"You'll be fine, Elizabeth," Mother says. She doesn't look at me.

Father crosses his arms and acts as if he hasn't heard me. "Try it again," he says, and Elizabeth looks away from me.

■

Allen was a senior, and he didn't talk to me until two weeks before midwinter break, after a choir concert at which I sang a solo. When he did, he said I had a beautiful voice and that I was beautiful, too. Beautiful, he said. Not hot or sexy or one of the other dozen things the boys at church hissed at me when Pastor Lewis wasn't around. That word, beautiful, sounding so good, almost innocent, stopped me, made me look at Allen closely. He stood in front of me, shoulders slumped, the bow tie of his choir uniform lying unfastened around his neck. He was blushing.

I let him take me to the movies.

The first thing my parents wanted to know about Allen was what church he went to. They knew me well enough to know I wouldn't bring home anyone but a good Christian boy. Allen laughed when I told him about the necessary ruse, but when I sat mute, studying the jagged edge of one of my fingernails, he seemed to realize I wasn't joking.

"You've never done this before, have you?" he asked.

"Dated a non-believer?" I looked up in time to see his eyebrows lift. That was what my father called people like Allen—the nicest term he used. I couldn't understand why it sounded so strange coming from my mouth.

Allen shook his head. "Lied to them."

I was sure I had, but I couldn't think of a quick example, and certainly nothing like this.

I told my parents he went to the Catholic Church on the other side of town. They weren't friends with any of the people who went there, which was a good thing, because Allen knew even less about Catholics than I did. Still, he must have performed well enough, because after having him over to dinner, my parents had a long whispered talk in their bedroom. I was supposed to be finishing my homework, but I waited outside their door, straining to hear their conversation, still unsure whether I wanted them to stop me or not. Allen was nice, but I was unsure how to act around him.

"She's growing up whether you like it or not," Mother said. "And she's going to start dating. At least she's doing it where we can see rather than sneaking around."

"No daughter of mine would sneak around," Father said. I took a step back from the door.

When they finally did come out, Mother smiled at me in a way I'd never seen before, and I realized this permission they were granting me was as much of a victory for her as it was for me. "Your father and I agree that being around you would be a good influence for Allen," she said, and behind her, Father's mouth curled in distaste. "Just be sure to invite him to church sometime. And maybe youth group?"

"Just don't let him touch you," Father said, then disappeared back into the bedroom.

■

I have never spoken to the woman next door though sometimes, after sitting in my room for hours, alone, I wonder what I might say to her some night, from my bedroom window, and I wonder why I never wondered these things before, why my house arrest has somehow connected my soul to the sound of her broom. Before, during all the years she's done this, I just ignored her or closed my window—something I can no longer bring myself to do, except during summer storms, when she isn't outside anyway.

A few weeks ago I watched as Elizabeth went next door to sell cookie dough for some church fundraiser I've been excluded from, but the woman wasn't home. I should have told Elizabeth not to bother, that I never see the woman until late afternoon, that I've decided the mornings must be when she sleeps, but I didn't think of it until later. Elizabeth probably would have gone anyway; she is the good Christian daughter, after all, and probably shouldn't be listening to me.

■

The purity ball was created to foster relationships between fathers and daughters in an effort to help young girls protect their virtue. There's a pledging ceremony at the end of the night where all the daughters present their fathers with a white rose, and it's supposed to be the culmination of the evening. It sounds good, fathers looking out for the well-being of their daughters, young girls having strong male role models. I still miss it in some ways, but even so, my favorite part of the evening was getting dressed up and not having to worry about boys staring at me, not with God's chosen men around me, not with Father there to protect me. Maybe, had things never happened between Allen and me, had I been allowed to go, I would have finally told him why I stopped wanting to go to youth group, and he would have believed me when I said I hadn't done anything to provoke those boys. He would have said *Okay* and kissed me on the forehead like he hasn't done since before Allen and I started dating.

I watch Elizabeth reach out to steady herself on the banister, and I wonder what she will think of this, her first time. I wonder what Father will say to her, whether he'll stick to the same script we followed every year, him laughing like he rarely does at home, or whether he will use the evening as further opportunity to lecture Elizabeth on all the evils my actions contain. "Be better than your sister," he might say. "See what happens when you don't let your father protect you."

At the bottom of the stairs, Father checks his watch and says they should have left five minutes ago. Mother runs through the living room and kitchen trying to find Elizabeth's misplaced shawl. Elizabeth beams at no one in particular, and I watch as her fingers toy with the clasp on her handbag—a bag just last year she used for playing dress up. No one notices me. I slink back to my bedroom and close the door, telling myself I should be happy Elizabeth is finally getting what she's wanted, that it's only fair it's my turn to be pushed to the side. I try not to consider that I might deserve this.

■

Allen and I didn't have sex on prom night, but I know that's what everyone thinks. He picked me up, we went to prom, we danced, we came home. On my front porch, he kissed the back of my hand because we thought my father might be watching.

By that point we'd been sleeping together for a month, usually at his house, but once at mine, when Father was at work and Mother was at Elizabeth's school conference. He said he wanted to see what it was like. I didn't know what he meant, but I shrugged and went along with it. He hadn't pushed or asked unkindly—he never did—and I was unprepared for how to respond. It was horrible, lying there, straining to hear the sound of the front door, voices coming up the stairs. Later, Allen suggested that we only do it at his house, saying it hadn't been as exciting as he'd expected, and I tried not to sound too relieved when I agreed.

The condoms, too, were his idea, not something I'd even considered. He said they would keep us safe, would stop anything bad from happening.

On prom night, Father met us at the door, just as Allen was lowering my hand from his lips. Allen smiled at him before walking back to his car, the same smile that had convinced them he was such a nice boy. "You're not to see him anymore," Father said, then he told me to go to my room. Mother came up a few hours later.

"Pastor Lewis saw Allen," she said, and she seemed to be choosing her words carefully. She didn't meet my eyes. "At the checkout." I didn't bother to lie or defend myself. My parents were convinced God led him to the grocery store that day, so I could be saved. There wasn't anything to say to that.

■

The woman next door only leaves her house once a week, on Tuesday afternoon. She buys groceries, I guess, because she has to eat and she never has any visitors, not even the mailman coming to the door to deliver a package. I sit at my window and watch her house, trying to peer in through the slats of the blinds, to see a sign of life within. I like to imagine that when she leaves for her weekly excursion, she goes to visit someone.

I wish I had the courage to steal the broom from the kitchen pantry and sneak out to help her one night. I wouldn't even have to speak to her, just stand beside her and begin on a new patch of sidewalk, our strokes timed perfectly, doing all the talking we need.

■

An hour after Father and Elizabeth leave together, Mother comes to visit me in my room—something she has rarely done since this all began. She seems taller without my father next to her. She sits next to me on the bed and takes one of my hands in hers. I want to ask her why she's here—not here in my room, but here in this life. She must have been someone else before, maybe even someone like me. Perhaps this, then, is what I will become—a quiet wife and someone's lesser half.

"How are you feeling?" she asks.

Isn't it obvious, I want to say, but I shrug instead, focusing on a piece of lint that has attached itself to her shoulder.

"Would you like to watch a movie?" she asks.

I don't, and I say so. Perhaps if Father were still here, I would go downstairs with her, and we would make popcorn in the hot air popper. Her gesture, timed as it is so that he's gone, means little to me. I know she's trying, but it isn't enough.

She leaves a few minutes later, pausing in the doorway to turn around and look at me. "It'll be okay," she says.

"Will it?" I ask. "Do you really believe that?" I put as much scorn in my voice as I'm able, and my mother gives a small jerk. I've hurt her, but for once I'm unrepentant. Whatever it is she's feeling now, it's only a piece of what I hold. She swore to love and honor her husband, but what about me? She stands in the doorway for a few more seconds before finally leaving, and a few seconds later I hear the bedroom door close behind her. Anger grows inside me. It feels hot, like I've heard it described but never quite believed. This emotion is my father's domain; mine is temperance. I want to study the feeling, step back and analyze it, but it's eating at me, and I can't detach myself, can't control myself, and so I let it overwhelm me, pull me under.

The broom is in the kitchen pantry, where it has been for as long as I can remember, but seeing it stops me short. My hand shakes slightly as I reach for its handle. There is no one to stop me. The front door swings gently closed behind me. I wish my father were here so I'd be walking away from him, too.

■

Back on that night, after I changed out of my dress, after my parents went to bed, I snuck downstairs to use the kitchen phone. Allen was silent for a long moment during which I looped the phone cord around my wrist, over and over, pulling it so tight it left marks on my skin. He apologized first, then asked if there was anything he could do for me, and I said, "No, thank you." That wasn't what I meant at all, but I couldn't think of anything else to say. He didn't push the matter and we hung up a moment later.

On my way back up to my room, I saw Elizabeth's face appear in the narrow crack of her doorway. Her head was tilted so that I could only see one eye. We looked at each other for a moment, but then she blinked twice, quickly, and disappeared. I could hear her bed springs squeak as she climbed back into bed, leaving me standing there in the hall, alone.

■

The woman next door doesn't seem to notice me. She doesn't nod or look up when I stand next to her. I'm not sure what I'm supposed to be doing, so I turn my broom on a few pieces of dried grass near the edge of the sidewalk, trying to match her rhythm with my own. Next to me, she seems to be working on a perfectly clean patch of pavement. After a few minutes of this, she moves her broom to the next square of sidewalk, carefully avoiding the crack. We work like this until long past the streetlights come on.

"Does your father know you're out here?"

In all the time I've lived next door to this woman, I've never heard her speak. Her voice is deeper than I imagined, but fuller, too. It seems to resonate even in this open space. I wonder if she was ever a singer. I still my broom and turn to face her. She is still watching the progress of her own broom.

"Yes," I say, because I don't want to get in trouble.

She lets out a sharp laugh. I blush.

"He's not home," I say.

"An even better reason."

I don't know what she means, so I nod, though I know she can't see. A few more moments pass in silence save for the sweep of her broom on pavement and, once, the distant bark of a dog. I wish Allen would drive by so that he could see me out here, though I'm no longer helping but simply watching her. She doesn't appear to notice, or perhaps she doesn't care.

"Why do you do this?" I ask. The question has been burning in me for months. I thought I would be able to see, to understand, if I stood next to her, but I'm just as confused as ever. That's not why I ask, however. I want to have knowledge that is mine and mine alone, something that can't be taken away, by anyone.

She looks up finally, leaning slightly on her broom. One of her eyes doesn't open quite as far as the other and the left side of her nose seems rather flat. They are small things, but the asymmetrical cast to her face makes me take a step back, and in that moment I'm sure that if God decides to punish me for one thing this night, it should be this.

She shows no sign that she noticed my aversion, but she doesn't answer. I wait for her to tell me how the solitude, the repetitiveness clears her mind, how every day she tells herself she won't go back to it but every night, she gives in. Or, perhaps, she will turn the question back on me, ask why I sit alone in my room all day, sit quietly at the dinner table with my head bowed as I pretend to pray, sit at my bedroom window each night and wish I were her.

Still she says nothing. We stare at one another, and I'm sure she's holding back on purpose. I no longer know why I came out here to join her. It seems like such a childish and pointless thing to do.

The flash of headlights finally pulls my eyes away from the woman, and I take a step back toward the shadows of her house. My father pulls the car into our driveway and walks around to the passenger door. I don't know what time it is, but I'm sure he and I used to stay out later.

"Wake up," he says to Elizabeth. He doesn't shake her, doesn't brush the hair back from her face. He doesn't touch her at all. Still, there's warmth in his voice and, I imagine, a smile on his face. "You're a big girl. You can walk yourself inside."

I know what she's thinking. She's tired. She wants him to carry her but knows asking will accomplish nothing, will reduce her in his eyes, and in this moment, she is all he sees.

The woman stands right next to me. She looks at me, and for the first time, I don't want to know what she's thinking.

The car door slams and the voices trail off as my father and sister move toward the door. I can only hear pieces of their conversation now: "fun" and "love" and "can't imagine" and, right before they go inside, Elizabeth's voice says my name, "Emma," though maybe she's saying *I'm a*, like *I'm a very lucky girl.*

CONJECTURE IN THE EARLY MORNING

KELLY A. WILSON

I have questions for you,
your figurine that dimly moves
away as I stare at the rounded edge
of the wooden chest, the meeting
of two perpendicular surfaces,
the stack of coasters that sit
on top, twelve tea candles
unlit, the marks of teeth
in an uneaten apple,
peripheral vision of a television
woman talking in the sliding glass

door, her picture in the metal
frame, the glare of light on glass,

and I can see something shapeless
on the other side, a reflection by chance,
light and right timing, my own
insecurity, but I cannot form the words
I need to say, only conjecture—the scratched
out shirt stain, the shard of debris
in your eye, the faint vacuum sound, high
resting heart rate, burning underneath.

It's suspicious the way the world looks
in the first few minutes of morning,
the color of circumvention, scattered dots
scrambling on a signal-less television screen.
I watch closely to discern a pattern
in the movement, but you hate mirrors
and the reflective properties of light
so you spend your mornings black in
the bathroom and the closet, shutting off,

as long as possible, the fact of another day,
directionless as the dots. I watch and know
I should see the pattern, but it is too dark to be sure.

APOLOGY

KELLY A. WILSON

Maybe it was the french fries
smashed and hardened in the door jamb.
Maybe we were running late again—too late
to stop—mom and me in front, and the boys in back—
all five of us spinning in the daily brother-regimens
of baseball and football and basketball games.

Maybe I heard the brakes my feet
could feel give way beneath the carpet
when the back seat crying started up again.
My arm stretched backhand sideways
to reach my little brother's mouth.
I hated the clumsy plastic rattling

his car seat made and how my hands
crunched between and underneath
the seats to find his fallen pacifiers,
the spit-cleaned everything
transparency of what he did to get his way.
He was hungry and so was I. It was July

in Indiana and the seats were the kind of burgundy
leather that makes your legs sweat,
when I realized there was nothing outside
my mother's window and my head swelled
with the stillness buckled in the passenger seat
where I sat beside her, bones fidgeting inside

my crossed legs and folded hands until my mind
was filled with so much blood that hated her minivan
life that it finally turned me inside out and I said aloud
I hoped I would never—*never*—be like my mom.
And so that never-say-never-word I truly meant—it cut

my mother's heart out of my heart and made a dark crawlspace.
My apology is not unlike the background country songs

with all the broken record Os in their *tomorrows*.
My mother knew that song, and sang the chorus
in her version of their twang. She seemed so happy
to love the nonsense words those awful baseline voices
were compelled by patterns to repeat, unquestioningly,
the same inscrutable causality—

       I expected to get punished good that night
when dad got home from work. It was his job
to do that. But nothing would make me sorry
for what I said, the blood still pulsing in my head—
a capacity so dark inside my spit-cleaned heart's
perpetual apology.

EATING ALONE

MARK NEELY

When we drank most news was of each other—
a girlfriend run off, a scrape with a shithole officer,

the various lawns and beds and cells
where we'd wake up after the longer nights—

but sober, eating noodles from a plastic bowl
I get the television news—bone shrapnel

piercing packed cafes, soldiers rehabilitating
missing legs, children charred in incendiary strikes,

a mother cutting off her daughter's breasts
to ward off rapists. This madness

chewing off my ears. It's easier to live
small crisis by small crisis, to believe

if you didn't drink so much, or slept more,
or had one frank conversation with your father,

then your troubles would dissolve like frozen creeks
and disappear into a muddy river. Reared

by an indifferent planet, I crouched by my bed
knowing no good I ever did could

keep humans from torturing one another,
could even hold the glaciers together.

LORENZO IN HIS CUPS

MARK NEELY

Lorenzo was in good form—on Katherine
again, of whom he spoke highly,
as worms speak highly of the stars.

He spoke in great whiskey breaths,
working his long fingers over the table,
white teeth flashing in the barroom haze.

"In her blaze I would surely burn," he said.
"She makes the rest of us look televised.
If she'd have me I could give up drink."

This caught me off guard
and Katherine too,
who stepped out of the gloomy dark

to scold us, like a store owner
telling off shoplifting boys.
Lorenzo ordered a round

and for the toast said, "Health," although
his slurring made it sound like "Hell."
When he got going like this no one

could shut him up. Kate marched off,
annoyed down to her boots, but to her health
we kept on drinking nonetheless.

LOVE SONNET IN WHICH HEIDI = THAT INFANT ANIMAL AND I = THE TERRIBLE THING

NATHAN BLAKE

Let me slick your bangs with a shark's tooth. Let
us beg from a pick-up truck. The Mayans
believed to lie with the dead was to know
them, to peel the rind. Now I am sackcloth.
My warbonnet moults. I have held your hand
but not felt it. Something funny on your
tombstone would be the letter X. I am
war-zone. I am dirge. They brought you home wrapped
in a smallpox quilt. Heidi, I have roamed
this valley itching for some thunder. I
saw you stirring a pot of chamomile—
or was it daisies? Do you remember
the man in the moon? When he hanged himself?
How I reached to bring his body to you?

LOVE SONNET IN WHICH ABORTION ACTS AS RELATIONAL TROPE

NATHAN BLAKE

"We finger-banged in a cotton-field" is
what you told the nurse, shifted your stirruped
calves. I wrote your name twelve different ways on
the back of a dollar bill. I knew a
single fox in a field full of pumpkins
does not know the taste of this. Inside you,
a bean-bodied curd. A blip. It's like those
matryoshka dolls, unpack your body
to find a river inside the river.
I napped while you wore a saffron robe. We
might sleep together again, I dreamed. That
night I wanted to crawl around your mouth
where your anger roosted, stretch your throat like
egg yolk runs through a sea of copper hands.

LOVE SONNET IN WHICH HEIDI = BIRD BY PROXY

NATHAN BLAKE

We end in each others' beginnings is
what the Cassin's finch etched along its spruce,
aimed for morale but gave noise instead. I'm
embarrassed to say we knew Rome only
through postcards, saw the Chilcotins without
seeing them. There is an urgency for
all things, it seems. Dismantle offers of
wayfare. Ensconce your head when kindled. Bare
your chest toward the sea. I feel something
out beyond the field of right and wrong is
another field showered in Spanish moss
and party hats. Feather the dust to show
what tides have written there for the birds: We're
all match-sticks in the old sight of our Lord.

ONCE UPON A BASSINETTE

REBECCA COOK

This is her first smile after it's over, after she squeezed my rubbery body in her sleeve of iron, clamping down on my bones, stirring up my screams, the way she would always bear down on me, her fist tighter than tight around the pink of me. This is the crook of her arm cradling my soft spot head rising to a point, my yellow skin that required a three day stay, my blue-grey eyes flutter soft against the hospital sheets. This is the fourth day, a fuzzy blanket of girl beside the page wire fence, legs like matchsticks, five and a half pounds of promise. She will grow fat on mother's milk and sugar water, she will push out milk teeth and mountains of poo, poo filled with blood and no one knows this girl is dying. Here are the old photographs of the paper white skin against the bright blue blanket spread on a sea of summer grass. These are the colors of the dying girl, a swirl of cow's milk in her belly, weaned too soon, her mother's breast an empty ache in her mouth, the loss, the cord between them broken. Of course she didn't know, she couldn't feel her daughter slipping away, she couldn't hear when my granny told her the truth of it, she could only hear my father's *everything is fine, nothing is wrong,* and when I flopped rag-doll lifeless on the pillows propping me up, the red velvet seam on my face, only then did she take me away to the doctor. *This girl is dying, is almost dead,* the sterile nipple has come up empty, she is a hollow doll, a mask of little girl dread and for the rest of her life she will always be hungry, after they pierce the poor baby vein in her left temple, after they pump her full of blood, after they make her fresh as an almost daisy, a yellow-fluffed chick full of Similac, she will always search for suck, her lips closing around spoons and pennies, around straws and crayons, around pencils and cigarettes, around the hollowed out feeling of never enough.

Tell me again, Mama. Tell me again the baby me, the little girl sitting in a pail of putty, patty caking handfuls onto her head. Tell me again the powder in my throat, a white cloud of almost smothering. Tell me again the little tub on the back porch, tell me how you left me there, how I slipped under the surface. I was seven months old and I learned the true taste of water, the fish girl of me bubbling and frothing before you pulled me up from that second womb, that almost death, a thousand little deaths coming up in my throat, even now, even now the empty space where she once was, little girl blue twisted around her apron strings, perfect doll daughter pressed tight against her knees.

These are her sunburned hands, this is her palm pressed lightly against my forehead, this is my mother reaching for me, reaching back from a mound of ash in the baked Georgia clay. See how she gathers me up in her arms. I am the best daughter, I am her greatest hope, I am wrapped in bunnies and stars, I am a scratchy cotton towel. I am the solid reflection of her perfect soprano. I am a blue ball of girl and I will throw her the ball. She is just twenty-four. She has Marlo Thomas curls and an even, white smile. She catches the ball and laughs and when she laughs the whole world turns the color of sunshine. I am curled inside her, I float in the watery middle of her. I kick my feet deep inside her belly and when she moves, I move, and when her time is complete, when it's finished and done with on an early Sunday morning, a smoke blue sky of November, when the medicine clears from her fuzzy head, she calls me Becky, she puts me in a basket and sings Rock a Bye, she lays me in the cradle, she walks away and the world stops, the empty space between us filling up with my cries, calling her back to me, always back. I am the girl she dreamed of when she was nine years old, rocking her baby doll, the promise of me coiled deep inside her. I am waiting while she goes to school, while her father barks his morning song at her, while her mother spoons her a dose of honey and vinegar. I wait for her, a hardening shell of girl. I wait until the perfect afternoon in May when she picks me up and twirls my dizzy head around the yard, when she picks me up and glues me to her hip, my bootied feet dangling down. See how she sets me in the afternoon light, wipes my dirty face with her wetted thumb. I am crawling across the grass, I am following the shadow of her, the reflection of what it means to be her daughter, her tiny baby bunting. It's four o'clock. She is loosening me from her breast, my mouth is full of her, still full after all these years, the soft net of her hands holding me in the water, soft floating me around the kitchen sink. There is all the time in the world while she soaps up my chest, fingers lightly brushing my beating heart. There is all the time in the world for just us two.

Tell me again, Mama. Tell me again the world will always be the perfect circle of the two of us. Tell me again how I'll always fit in your mouth, how you'll polish me like a stone, how I am so shiny inside your smiling. Tell me again your hands smack smacking against my bare legs, me and my *darn, darn, darn* song coming around the side of the house. Tell me again how I'm a bad girl, a terrible baby smacking her own hands because she's bad, will always be bad. Tell me again how you swallowed me up, the perfect little girl of me. I am toddling around the house, I am searching for you, and there you are, hidden behind the door, just a game, just a full of tears game, a stop of the heart game, a game of the blue rubber ball tossed up so high.

There will never be enough afternoons, there will never be enough mother. Time will catch up with us, time will unroll a navy blue dress with white ruffles, a brown haired girl reaching for a piece of chicken because no one is watching, no one remembers her. She climbs up on the table, hands outstretched and the only mother in the world, the only mother with brown-blonde hair will scoop her up, will crush her in her arms, will hold her closer than close, and Mother, I am crawling into your lap again, I can smell your cold cream spell, I can feel your soft, soft hands closing around my own and it's the fourth day again, just home from the hospital, full of bunnies and stars, my fist curved around your ring finger, glinting in the afternoon sun.

PRESTIDIGITATION, PENNSYLVANIA

RUSTY BARNES

Magic in its backwoods,
a bloody star in a lit sky
that we call *anywhere*
so long as it isn't here.
Follow it and succeed,
stay and be damned.
Joe and Tammy on the school roof
gravel biting their sweaty palms.
Joe's 19 and been to college
about twenty miles away.

After Tammy reclothes her
soggy bottom half (pale in the moon)
he gives her the news:
*what we just did? It's called
a labial-digital fricative*. He laughs.
She says, *you're the dumbest
fuck of every dumbfuck that
ever left this town*. She snaps
her belt to with a motion denying
further talk and climbs the steam
pipe down. Joe lies back and smokes.
He thinks about Jesus and Intro to
Philosophy. Tammy's not set up
for these questions. He's born
to the idiocy of education. Jesus
Buddha Gandhi Peter Singer Thomas
Kuhn Aleister Crowley Ken Wilber, shit.

There's no savior in this town,
just Tammy's changeling eyes
and some rare magic that transmutes
kid to man before he's ready.

EVERYTHING PASSED BY SO QUICKLY

SCOTT PINKMOUNTAIN

We all had sisters
who were two or three years older.
They would walk around in towels for the benefit
of killing us, towels on their heads
and wrapped around their
oh dear gods.

We'd live in sitting
rooms waiting for the sprint or stroll
from bath to bedroom. We had nothing better
to do. Because there was
no better thing.
There was no thing at all.

THE YOUNG COUPLE GO ON SEPARATE VACATIONS

SERAH CARTER

She was presented to the Mutma, who had known her father, and called her Lily- though that was not her name. That night a guard came to her in her bed. The next day the Mutma offered her a kingdom. "For your son," he said.

There was no terminal four, no matter how much he argued with the attendants. He rolled his eyes, flared his nostrils, dropped his bags. Around him paper people passed, thankful that he was not one of theirs. "Sir, are you lost? Is there someone we can call?" He noticed too late that he had the wrong amount of fingers.

For a time she fell in love with a girl who did not have hair but rather lilacs which sprouted inexplicably in vines. They drank tea on a bright white balcony and watched the sun wilt the blossoms. She forgot how lips felt.

He couldn't recall the name of the city, where it had been, how long it had been there. He knew that the lighter he held belonged to the King, who was waiting for him. It was a city where everyone looked at their feet.

The natives made a hammock for her out of leaves and told her to keep an eye out for snakes. No one seemed surprised to discover her missing the next morning. The hammock swung in empty breeze. Eyes were painted on the trees.

The blanket he bought in the market by the sea began small. It grew in gloaming, the cross stitched people fighting, farming, fucking, bearing cotton faced babies in gingham houses. At the train station the blanket swallowed him whole but no one knew. The stitches anchored their feet to the ground.

She listened to the guide explain that there was a man in each village whose job it was to give the snowflakes that fell names. With pieces of slate and chalk, wearing long blue coats, they would go out and return in despair, their chalked names smudged by nameless flakes.

In the steep countryside they built their farms on the edge of open air so that burial was simply a matter of digging the hole and aiming correctly. The corpses made the tops of the grasses buzz together as they passed. They hit bumps, became airborne, banners. He clapped.

The child in the alleyway had the head of a hyena. He tried to rob her and she threw sticks for him. At night he sat on the other side of the wall and laughed. She told him he could outlaugh the stars. He asked her, "What is a star?"

At the outmost edge of a crumbling city not yet abandoned the old woman selling herbs asked him if this was what he really wanted. He looked at the rotting wood and creeping vines. The wide causeways had surrendered to dust. Decay had a sweet and cloying smell. He wished to bottle it.

The timekeepers measured hours by dropping stones in the churning dust of an inner courtyard. The stones were warm and smooth and round.

"But how do you know it's time?" she asked.

"The Will of our God Commands it." They replied.

She left with hours in her pocket.

They had agreed to meet at the fountain with the marble elephants. It was the place where they had first met, shared ice cream, argued into something like love. When they pass each other by, she thinks of hyenas. He thinks of blankets. Their trains will leave soon; lots of packing to do.

THE THEATRE OF THE FLOATING WORLD

SIMON JACOBS

I crossed the turnstiles and emerged from the rail station into the salty air. The beachfront was the image of some enormous celebration that had broken up years ago. Empty stretches of sand, here and there bits of plastic and rubber, discarded clothing, a broken bottle half-buried in the sand. Jutting up from the ground, naked wooden poles that had once pegged huge, neon tents, beneath which the last tatters of my generation had crowded to dance the night away before succumbing to oblivion. Very few of them were left. Anything of value had disappeared a long time ago. I wasn't much better off. I was here to pay for sex. I was as desperate as anyone else.

A hundred meters out on the water, the beach's only current attraction blotted the skyline: the three floating Japanese theatres. Three enormous, creaking rafts, tethered together and elaborately anchored to the sea floor, pitched imperceptibly back and forth with the waves, each bearing a theatre of a different size. The largest, the Loew, sat in the middle, yet tonight was the only one not illuminated. All three theatres shared a similar, lopsided character—the seating for the audience was all outdoors, but the stage was covered, the rafters hidden by an imposing proscenium arch that loomed over the first few rows. Beneath it, a walkway thrust out from the main stage like a tongue, upon which the climactic battles of feudal Japan were played out by kabuki actors in the thick of the audience. The wings, the dressing rooms, the riggings of it all were packed behind the stage, may even have descended into the underworks of the raft itself. What marvel of engineering kept these monstrosities afloat and mostly operational, no casual observer could say.

Walking the beach, it was best to follow the light. A little avenue of electric torches formed a path to the assortment of shacks on the waterfront, housing for the cast and crew. A tiny jetty stuck out into the shallows, to which several small boats were moored, meant to carry theatre patrons out to the rafts. A bald, heavyset Japanese man stood before the jetty, the guide to the stygian waters between me and the three floating theatres.

"You're here for the performance, then?" he said.

"Only in the most carnal, backstage sense," I replied.

He chuckled. "I see. Well." A long pause, filled with sea breeze, while he came up with a rejoinder. He licked his lips. "Mind you're delicate with our ingénues. They've three shows a night, you know."

"I'm actually looking for someone with variation in their twenty-third chromosome," I said.

It took him a few seconds to work this out. Then he smiled broadly. "Of course, sir. We would be only too happy to oblige your discerning taste. Might I recommend Shoji? One of the freshest additions to our cast. I believe he has this next performance free."

"Shoji sounds perfect," I said.

"And am I correct to assume, sir, that you'll be purchasing services for eight minutes?"

"Let's make it twelve. For the sake of romance."

He smiled again, put out his hand. "I am Mr. Ageda."

I shook it. Money changed hands. "Jones," I said.

"A true pleasure, Mr. Jones."

The configuration of theatre-rafts we called—pun absolutely intended—the "Theatre of the Floating World," after the urban, pleasure-seeker lifestyle of Edo Period Japan, during which kabuki first flourished. And for the Pacific, of course.

Mr. Ageda used a carabiner to hook our boat to a cable trolley, which ran along one of several cables leading from the end of the jetty to the first theatre, the Cameo. I sat in the back, the only passenger, as Mr. Ageda rowed. A bell hung off the front end of the boat, clanging dimly through the sea fog.

"If I may say so, it's not many of your age that we get around here," Mr. Ageda said.

I looked out at the water, suddenly not in the mood for conversation, although these days there wasn't much to do besides talk. "No?"

"No," he said, and then, as if I didn't understand the implication, "hardly any as young as you." Unable to resist, he turned to look at me, all pretense gone. "Mr. Jones, if you don't mind… exactly how old are you?"

"Twenty-six," I lied. "And I would appreciate at least a semblance of discretion about this on your part, Mr. Ageda."

He turned back around, spoke to the sea. "It's just that people tend to notice, is all."

"I know."

He rowed on.

Why did the theatres exist? Who knew. Some "brilliant" engineer's idea of what to do with an empty, liquid horizon. If one of the rafts detached and floated out to sea, taking its cast and crew with it—well, that might be kind of romantic. Bidding farewell to your mates on the shore. Members of your cast leaping from the deck floorboards sleeves trailing into the black sea.

"Shoji performs in the Roxie, our most modestly-sized venue," Mr. Ageda said after a while. "That's the third one." He pointed.

When our boat arrived at the Cameo, a performance was in full swing. A gargantuan, elaborately costumed man in drooping red and white sleeves strutted down the stage's walkway, his white face striped with red, his severe features exaggerated in black outline. Wooden blocks clapped together in the background, the rhythm for his movements. The tempo increased, added the frantic plucking of a shamisen; my heartbeat quickened. The actor on stage stomped his foot once and struck a pose.

A voice from the crowd bellowed, "Yamashita!"

Cheering, applause erupted from the audience. Most were on their feet, waving their fists and hats in the air.

Mr. Ageda unlatched the carabiner and transferred it to an adjacent cable. In a few seconds, the stage had drifted from view and we were on our way towards the second theatre.

"That was *Shibaraku*," he said. "It has always been one of our most popular performances. Have you ever seen a kabuki play before, Mr. Jones?"

"Yes. Several times."

"Really? At what venue? In this day and age there must not be many."

"Here."

This caught him up. "Ah. I'm sorry. I thought I would have remembered you."

The Loew was the largest of the three theatres. A landing where the boat could dock led at an incline up to the platform, empty and silent in the moonlight, the area beneath the proscenium black like a gaping mouth, threatening to engulf everything around it. A glimmer near the top where, true to the theatre's old Broadway namesake, a buddha sat in the arch above the stage, watching benignly over the nonexistent audience. The entire structure groaned. I thought I could see it sway. Water lapped at the edges of the landing, itching to take it back. "Temporarily closed for repairs," Mr. Ageda said.

He switched the carabiner to another cable. This one was slick from the fog, and the trolley moved erratically, sliding back and forth as our boat progressed across the water.

"Would you ever consider joining our coterie, Mr. Jones?" Mr. Ageda asked.

"I'm not Japanese."

He just chuckled.

At the Roxie, the last theatre in line, young men carried painted and varnished wooden backdrops into place and adjusted lighting on the stage. A few spectators had arrived early for the next performance and were catcalling at the stagehands. Mr. Ageda docked our boat. We climbed onto the platform. "I'll take you to the back, then," he said.

I followed him backstage, through a watertight aluminum door, down a short staircase and into a dense, transforming maze of sliding translucent dividers and narrow corridors that connected to the wings and dressing rooms. Pipes ran along the wood paneling, but even following them I lost all sense of direction. We stopped suddenly, and Mr. Ageda knocked once on an unlabeled door before pushing it aside. We stepped into a tiny dressing room.

The young man I presumed to be Shoji sat on his knees on a pillow, facing a half-length mirror. Jars of powders and makeup were scattered around it. Garishly colored fabric was piled in a corner, the night's costume. His head was shaved, and he wore an off-white t-shirt and shorts. He turned when he heard the door. I knew, then, that this would not be just an anonymous encounter. He looked younger than I was.

"Shoji? This is Mr. Jones. Mr. Jones, Shoji. He has twelve minutes."

Standing, Shoji was a head shorter than me. He came over and shook my hand. "Nice to meet you."

Mr. Ageda jerked his head to the right.

Shoji nodded once. "I'll go and get ready." He stepped through a door on the righthand wall and shut it behind him.

Mr. Ageda looked at the clock above the mirror. "I will return for you at 9:38, Mr. Jones."

"Wait—do his preparations count against my time?"

He shrugged and backed out through the door we'd come through. I took off my shirt and belt, then paused, unsure of what to do.

Shoji returned a minute later, his hairless chest bare, holding a small tube. He knelt on his knees in front of me, undid the front of my pants and slid down my boxers. He squeezed a little lubricant onto his index finger and rubbed it down the length of my penis.

A wordless exchange, and we had fallen to the floor. I grabbed his head with one hand, felt the bristle of a day's growth of hair. Ran my fingers down the back of his neck, then took hold of both shoulders. The beginnings of sweat on his back. Pores opening. His body beginning to shine. I eased myself into him from behind. Began the motion of the hips and the penis for which I had paid so substantially. Only here, in this dressing room, this was the only place where there wasn't enough time. While others gathered a few meters or miles away to sit through a five-hour kabuki performance, I fucked for five minutes as if fighting for my life.

Our position allowed me to see Shoji's face in the mirror. His eyes were shut, his lips tight in a grimace. I paused, out of breath. "Are you all right?" I panted.

Shoji opened his eyes. "I'm okay."

"Are you sure?"

"Yes. Go." His rear gave a little bump backwards, as in: Get it over with.

"Could you spread your legs out a little further, please?"

"Yes." He scooted outwards with his knees; I wondered if they were bruised.

"Thanks." I pushed myself further into him as I continued. The seconds ticked on. There on the floor, as I fucked him, a warmth came over me. Mentally, I crossed some sort of threshold, and I wrapped one arm around Shoji's waist and began to jerk him off. I glanced in the mirror, and wished we'd readjusted to somewhere I couldn't see him. He was biting his lip, looking fixedly at the floor. I imagined it rocking up and down in his vision. I kept up the pace until I came, but after I did, I stayed inside of him, continued to masturbate Shoji until he came as well, after another minute or so. He was very quiet. I didn't even notice that he'd come until I felt it on my hand.

We lay naked on the floor afterwards, pressed together, my hands clasped at his chest. Facing away from me, he'd said nothing. I kissed his neck. One more minute passed. He said he had to start dressing for his next performance, made motions to leave me. I held him tighter.

"No, wait—stay here. Mr. Ageda told me you had the next performance off."

"I don't. I have to get ready."

"Let me help."

"You should go," he said.

"What play are you doing?"

"*Sonezaki Shinjū.*"

"The love suicides. That's my favorite."

"Then you should buy a ticket to see it."

"I will." I squeezed him. "Can I see you after?"

"I don't think so."

"Please."

"I don't think so."

"Even if I pay?" My voice wavered.

"Talk to Mr. Ageda."

Then, perhaps because in reality I was only twenty years old, and as much as I tried to deny it still felt everything, I said to Shoji, with an aching intensity that threatened to trickle over the edge, "Come back with me."

"I'm sorry, Mr. Jones," he replied to the floor.

"No, don't call me that—it's Justin. Call me Justin."

"I'm sorry, Justin. I can't."

"You can't or you don't want to?"

He didn't answer.

A shuddering intake of breath. I felt dangerously close to tears, and it scared me. "I live inland, Shoji. You know, LA, the empire. We could still—"

A sharp knock on the door jarred me. "Your time is up, Mr. Jones." The door slid open and Mr. Ageda stepped in. "Come along now."

I leaned in close, kissed Shoji's cheek. "Come with me," I whispered.

"That's enough, Mr. Jones."

I held him for one more second.

"Mr. Jones." I felt the sharpness of his voice in my stomach.

I let Shoji go, collected my clothes, and got to my feet. Mr. Ageda averted his eyes as I pulled my pants on. "I'll take you back. Shoji, clean up and get dressed. Akiko will come to help with your makeup."

I looked at Shoji, lying on his side, his legs pulled up to his chest. "Bye," I said, and stepped into the hallway. Mr. Ageda shut the door, and seeing Shoji vanish behind it I thought that something had just irrevocably ended, and that I had missed it.

As Mr. Ageda led me brusquely down unfamiliar corridors back to the deck, I swallowed to keep my voice even and said, "I'd like to buy a ticket to the next performance."

"I don't think so, Mr. Jones. I think it's time for you to leave."

"No—I'll pay you extra, I'll—" Frantic, I reached into my pocket and withdrew a roll of bills, held them up.

Mr. Ageda swatted my hand away. "Theatre tickets cost more than sex out here, Mr. Jones. And I would strongly advise you against trying to elope with any more of our actors. I could've told you this would happen. You're too young. You don't understand these things."

Mr. Ageda cranked open the watertight door leading to the deck, and I was hit with a gust of cold air. Other boats had arrived since we'd gone backstage, and the seats were almost full.

"Just let me watch the first scene," I pleaded.

"He's not in the first scene."

"I don't care. Please." A part of me imagined Shoji taking the stage early, in his pure white makeup, seeing me, reaching out to me. A bigger part—the part that had been exactly here so many times before—knew better, knew that they'd never stray from the script, that the play would be exactly the same tonight as it was last night and would be the night after. The part of me that wanted everyone to keep acting, to stave off something horrible.

Mr. Ageda led me along the edge of the platform, towards the dock. People eyed us from their seats. A man stepped into our path and held out an arm. "Been back visiting with the cast, eh? A little pre-show tête-à-tête?" He laughed, a gruff, seen-it-all laugh. "It's a contextual pleasure, innit? Backstage?" He laughed and clapped me jovially on the back.

I jerked away, as if he sought to infect me. "Keep your fucking hands off me."

He raised his hands, took a step back. "Whoa. Keep a calm head, boy. Shit."

I turned desperately to Mr. Ageda, grabbed his hand. The smaller, younger part of me took over. "Please, Mr. Ageda. Just one scene. I'll stand off to the side. And then I'll go. I promise. Please."

"Wants to see his girlfriend onstage, eh?" the man said. "Come on, Ageda. Let the boy live. It'll be his only chance."

Mr. Ageda sighed. "Follow me."

He took me to the back, behind the last row of seats, at the edge of the raft. "You may observe from here," he said. "During the first intermission, I take you back to the shore. No arguments. Got it?"

I nodded. "Yes. I understand."

I swear I felt the raft shift beneath my feet. Fifteen minutes later, the lanterns on the edge of the platform dimmed and the stage lit up. Woodblocks collided rhythmically, building slowly. Growing in volume as the audience joined in, clapping, whooping. A spotlight centered on the stage. The banging reached an anguished frenzy; a final, emphatic *clack*—and it's gone. I bite my lip. A curtain withdraws. The play begins.

THE SHIP'S SING COOK

TERRANCE OWENS

The cook sings into his boil—easy
with the meat. Milk and honey
are wrung from the day.
He undresses the garlic,
pixilates the tomato, the onion
opens like the sea.
His hand is sure,
his fine knife; his initials are carved
in the carving board, and sweat
waits for a high note at the tip
of his nose. Land Ho! there is nothing
more believable than earth
stewing in his pot.

UGLY FISH

TERRANCE OWENS

We think Grandma has gone
just a little crazy.
She brings fish
for Thanksgiving,
but no one says a word.
Jack thinks,
ugly fish,
and Grandma's vowels
are shaped like gourds.
Poor Grandma,
poor fish
caught slap-happy, slump-puckered
in the raunch of the dark shore.
And if I tumbled through wreaths of light & stone
what shadows would come
wobbling from my mouth?
Mirk. Mimble. The moon
pulls from us.

CROSSWORD

SOMMER BROWNING

Across

1. Eat a bag of _____
10. _____ toe
16. Mother-in-law (adj.)
25. Where you'll spend your golden years
31. Something you claim is in your past
63. Some Oprah bullshit
80. Gosling, but not gosling
87. Fermented liquid that makes everything better
94. God of marriage
111. _____ life or _____ choice
147. The Ponzi scheme of diets
154. Color you're either supposed to wear or not wear after that holiday you can't remember
166. Something you can't afford but desperately need
174. Exercise one mainly finds in India and white people neighborhoods
184. Yoko _____
191. When we were kids _____ Maid was a game
202. A staple of the spa and porn industry

Down

1. Something you found in your mom's drawer when you were 8
2. On the rocks
3. Reasons for painful cramps
10. What marriage and insane asylums have in common
11. Where my ladies ____?
12. Douchebag degree you should have gotten
14. Internet star I'm too old to know about but somehow do thanks to that New Yorker article
35. How you felt after that week in NOLA you can't remember
66. Classier way to say one-night stand
67. How long a marriage lasts and/or feels
87. Late night sex date or, if you're married, dialing the phone with your butt
91. Distilled liquid that makes everything better
98. What you should have said
154. Another word for something that feels good
155. _____ Solo
156. Something I'm too poor to understand
176. Never heard of it

MOTHER FORGETS CHURCH

CHERYL & JANET SNELL

mother forgets "church"
and a hush smothers us

in her brain's atrium
a processional of tangles
son brother husband father

where's the church and where's the steeple

she wanders empty eyed
through the basilica to the transept of a cross
all dressed up since 2 AM

TOUGH ROOM

CHERYL & JANET SNELL

In the room, she eyes
the exit. Next week
she won't come, next week
they'll miss her. Well. Some will.
Some don't—outside the context
of the room she doesn't know
who her friends are
and so searches aimlessly,
sometimes for years, until she forgets
what she was looking for. She would like to
return to the room to start over
but others just like it have sprung up.
She enters the idea of the room instead
where strangers fill the seats inside her head.

They must have expected something fresh
after the big build-up. They'd never have come
if they'd known she'd already come full circle
beginning again at exactly the point at which
she'd been interrupted.

JASON LOOK

D.W. LICHTENBERG

Jason look, *she* said to him. *She* had a plaid sun dress on, loose at the chest, as was the style I think.

Jenny was next to *her*. Jenny was wearing a dress not so different from *hers*. Straight collar. Thick straps. Slip-on shoes. Jenny looked to where *she* was pointing. Jason didn't. He was sort of in the middle of a big conversation with me.

I wasn't really listening. I was watching *her* walking next to Jenny. They were walking in front of Jason and me. We were both wearing skinny jeans and t-shirts, as was the style I think.

Jason, look at that building. Jason, *she* said. Isn't that horrible? A place like that, *she* said, it just looks absurd, you know? In this neighborhood. In Brooklyn. In Williamsburg. Every building is six stories high. *She* was pointing to a big skyscraper on the edge of McCarren Park.

Jenny squinted in agreement. Yeah, and they couldn't of made it uglier. Fuckin silver and all that.

Later, we were back at Jason & *her* place. They were pretty horny I guess, and went straight to the bedroom. Jenny and I sat around for a bit, then she took me into the bathroom and we made out a little. She gave me a hand job too. She was weird like that, always trying to prove to me she was a great girlfriend or something. I don't think she was ever actually my girlfriend, though. I think she just pretended she was, or I pretended she was, or something.

She and Jason came out after a half hour and we had some beers. Jason had some weed and offered me some, but I said I wasn't really in the mood. Not in the mood? he said. He was like that, trying to emasculate me in front of the girls. I think he knew I was into his chick and that's why. I think he sort of looked up to me too. Like I was the big mystery to him. He went on until one of the girls told him to pass the pipe.

So what's good with the biz these days? I said to him. He worked in an office. I only mentioned his job to him to make him pissed.

The biz? What the fuck is the biz man? Fuck you and your smugness. He took a hit and passed it to Jenny. Jenny took a hit and passed it to *her*.

You know, I said. Don't you work in business? Like, you help manage accounts at a hedge fund.

You seem to know a lot about it, man. Jason smiled. I shrugged. Jason had a great apartment. The kinda place you could play hide & seek in.

Yeah you know, I said. Everybody knows something. I don't know much but I know something. Hedge funds, what do I know, I said. I had the habit of being smug without really wanting to be.

Well, Jason said, well fuck that man. The age of the hedge fund is over, right? I'm nothin but a dinosaur. About as much of a dinosaur as the guy who still wants to write the great American novel. It's all quiet these days so you can wipe that goddamn smirk off your face.

That put a pause in things. Jenny cut the edge a little: Oh so guess what? I got commissioned to do this painting. Commission is like crap, barely enough to cover my supplies and all. Oh and I'm pretty sure that the dude like... wants on me.

It happens, *she* said to Jenny. Buying a painting is about the same as buying a drink for a girl. To some guys, that is. (*She* looked at Jason just then.)

Jenny was pretty good looking. Well, Jenny was real good looking. A little heavier, not skinny like *she* was (like the style was). Not that it mattered, really, I mean Jenny had the body. The style wasn't to have the body. But that doesn't stop anybody from liking the body.

What kind of painting? I said. I think Jenny'd told me already but I wanted her to think I cared. Or maybe I wanted her to think I didn't care and wasn't listening. Not really sure.

Jenny said she'd explain it but didn't want to bore anybody.

Bore? *she* said. It's hard to be bored. If you really think about it.

Yeah, Jenny said, that's true. Jenny probably didn't have any idea what *she* was talking about. I sure as hell didn't. Jenny had this habit of returning the favor.

You know? *she* said, continuing. The other day I was at my mom's for the holidays. And one day she comes home with this big box under her arms. And I ask her, what in hell is that mom? Because she isn't exactly rich and doesn't often come home with large boxes out of nowhere. And she set the box down on the table and opened it, smiling. She showed me what was inside and it was a microwave. And she had this smile, just this glow, you know? And I said, hey you already have a microwave, mom. And she says to me, well, yeah, but this is a microwave **and** toaster. And she had this glow. This smile that was telling me, this is the solution to all our problems! This smile that was telling me everything.

She paused. Jenny and Jason laughed a little at *her* story.

I was pretty good looking too. Not that it mattered, I was pretty crap with the girls. I mean, when I really wanted something I would go for it. But nil on the casual encounters. I wanted *her*. And I was pretty convinced I could get *her*.

Maybe it was just that I was bored. Seems like all I did was sit around, drink, maybe smoke pot, maybe sleep with Jenny, I don't know. Talk shit about a pretty sunset. Sex up a really bad piece of art. Pretend to like really shit music, anything the blogs liked. Anyone you could see for eight dollars in a basement, with a bar that sold Pabst Blue Ribbon, Bass Ale, Schmidt's. Ride a bike because it was hardcore. Smoke cigarettes because life was shit. Or because otherwise people wouldn't know you knew life was shit (but not in the trite lifeisshit I'mgoingtostoplivingit way— in the theoreticallylifeisshit I'mgoingtocynicallymakefunofit way).

And BBQs. Not barbecues. B-B-Qs. In the concrete backyard. With a coal grill like a typewriter. Likeatypewriter. Nobody knew what to do with the coal, but it happened. On the concrete slab with Christmas lights strung up. Strung out.

Shit, I don't know what. What did you want them to do? Get day jobs? Most of them had day jobs, I think. I think actually the reason they were all so absurd, me included, was because they were guilty about their day jobs for chrissake. Embracing whatever nobody else wanted to embrace. That's what the style was those days. That was style.

And I wanted *her*. Jenny was nice but pathetic and boring and not for me or maybe just plain notforme. Jenny was one of those people who painted because she was arty, not because she was a painter. Because she was raised arty her whole life by two wannabe hippies. In Princeton. To Jenny arty was just normal shit and painting was a normal job with goals that were attainable over time as long as one worked hard, worked consistent, didn't just give up. Which was fine. Just not for me notforme.

Jason's girl was flamed. *She* had these streaks of rage. *She* didn't make any sense at all. Like when *she* was going on about that skyscraper. *She* knew *she* was the gentrification *she* was pointing at.

One time *she* called me up on the phone. I don't know if *she* was on something or what. I thought probably, but these days I think probably not. These days I think *she* was probably just, you know.

There was loud music playing. And it was one of those bands, you know. The ones the bloggers blogged about. They sold out basements, had to upgrade to churches and parks. *She* was going on about this song. I forget what the song was. That stuff went in and out in weeks.

This shit could just go on all night fucking long, *she* said to me. Just this one part, the beat, and that synth hook, over and over. And I'd be dancing, *she* shouted, hell yeah. It could just keep going— you know what I mean?

Yeah, I responded, yeah for ten minutes at least.

Dude, *she* said back, fuck it.

Yeah, I said, you're right, thirty minutes at least... and I agree with your fuck it sentiment.

Fuck all, *she* responded. Fuck all. I wanna dance, *she* said. I am dancing, *she* said. Then I heard the phone fall to the ground.

That was maybe the first time I decided that *she* dug me. That was a pretty personal moment, I figured. Maybe not though. I mean, that was sort of the style those days. To just say— fuckitmanwe'reallinthistogether. Fuck it life's such a fucking joke. Fuck me, fuck you, fuck everybody, I am a selfish prick. And so on andsoon.

Later that week, we were at a bar. We hadn't planned on it. It was one of those joints right on Bedford so it was no surprise seeing somebody you knew. But also I was basically hoping *she* would walk in.

You still with that fuck head? was the first thing I said to *her*.

You still with that beezie? *she* said back. I think *she* knew I half hated Jenny. And even though *she* had this infatuation with Jason, I knew *she* was bored with him, just stuck on the infatuation, not the guy.

We laughed. We talked. Etc etc. I liked to flirt with girls. Usually I didn't care if the girl wasn't single. I was a dick and often figured I'd win her over. And with *her*, well it was really hitting me hard that I dug *her*. All of a sudden. Suddenly, even.

Later, *she* asked me about my writing, said *she'd* seen a poem of mine in a magazine. I didn't like talking about it and changed the subject. You wanna go do something crazy? I said.

Okay.

You don't ask what it is before you agree to it?

How much do I have to lose? I lost it all when I was eleven. I got nothing.

By this time, we'd both had a few. But I mean who hadn't had a few? It was what people did around there. Like taking the subway. Like taking a digital picture to remember the moment. Because the moment didn't last forever.

It's the fucking moon, *she* said to me as we walked down the street. Of course it's beautiful. It has no other choice. No other way to be.

The clouds floated over the moon. Like water rippling over a sunken flashlight in a river. It was the moment I knew I dug *her* for sure. The moment I knew I wanted *her*. Those things always seemed to happen over full moons. Over sunken flashlights.

Well, I responded, I was just saying. You don't gotta talk shit about the moon.

Somebody's gotta do it. Might as well be me.

So we went to my place and I said, Here's the crazy thing.

I pointed to the ladder on the side of my building that went up five flights to the roof. It shook like crazy as we climbed, and I climbed second and stared at *her* ass.

We got up there and from the top you could see all the half-built luxury condo buildings. You could see at least six. Skeletons, just guts.

And I said to *her*, Let's jump it.

And we jumped it, to the closest skeleton, just a few feet off. And we walked through what would have been an investment banker's half million dollar loft, except I don't know if it ever was, considering the housing bubble and the fall of investment banking and all.

She was looking off into Manhattan. And *she* said it was like a Lite Brite board. And *she* said it was something crazy, didn't I think? And I did.

And *she* shouted, I am a product of my environment! into the distance. *She* yelled it at Manhattan. And then *she* yelled, There's a difference between being part of culture and defining it! Then *she* sat, her legs dangling.

You know how in movies, *she* said to me, there's always this point where the two people fall out, and then in the next fifteen minutes something forces one of them to save the other from something? And there's that turn. That change.

Yeah, I said.

You know how, you know how like you never really feel it?

Yeah, I said.

Like, you know, even though you can see what was supposed to change it all and redeem their friendship, it just doesn't fit. Because silence kills everything.

Yeah, sort of, I said.

Well, *she* continued, well I was thinking we should have sex. And then never talk again. Just to prove Hollywood wrong, you know?

Yeah, sure, I said.

And then after a bit I said, You know, yeah. Yeah. What the hell.

Come on, let's fuck, *she* said. And *she* made towards my roof.

Wait, let's do it here, I said. I was afraid if *she* jumped we'd lose each other somewhere between there and my bed.

Okay, fine, *she* agreed.

And we fucked there on the steel beam. I was afraid of cumming too soon. There wasn't too much room and there was always the risk of losing our balances and falling, but really *she* was gorgeous out there and I was just nervous.

We didn't say anything for a while. I wasn't sure how serious *she* was about the neverspeakingagain so I didn't say anything. But eventually *she* said we should go downstairs and make some tea.

Do you have any green tea, *she* asked me. And I told *her* yes, I did have some green tea. Then we went down and had some. And I was pretty sure we hadn't lost each other on the way down.

A lot of things get lost in silence, *she* said as *she* drank her tea.

Huh? I said, pretending I hadn't remembered *her* telling me that silence kills.

She was gone in the morning, and Jenny was there a few hours later.

We fucked. I wasn't nervous around Jenny and it was all right. And then I told her we had to stop doing this to ourselves.

Doing what to ourselves, Jenny asked.

You know.

No. What?

Fucking.

Fucking ourselves?

Yeah, exactly.

And then she kept on asking me what in hell I was talking about. I think she knew it was over but she stayed there in bed for a while. And we smoked cigarettes even though I always told her I didn't like smoking in the house because as soon as I made a habit of smoking in the house, I'd be admitting to myself that I reallyhadanaddiction on my hands. In my hands. In everyone's hands. It was the style those days.

Jason's girl had a thing with keeping *her* mouth shut. *She* couldn't was the thing, as should've been obvious to me. But not so much for whatever reason. And for other reasons Jason ended up messing me up pretty bad.

Which was all right because Jenny took it up to take care of me for the next week while I skipped out on work. We had good sex and watched every Roman Polanski film in order. I was hit pretty hard by his first movie. Nothing really happens, except this lady cheats on her husband with a hitchhiker. There's a moral dilemma and it's wrapped up pretty poorly, wrapped with the cartoons section of the Times, holes in it, the works.

By the time we got past the murder of his wife, "Chinatown," "The Tenant," the consensual rape of a thirteen year old girl, and the Holocaust, "Oliver Twist" was weirdly dark. Not surprisingly dark. Because I mean, of course it was gonna be dark. Weirdly dark. As in, whatisthismoviereallyabout? dark.

And not to mention "Rosemary's Baby." Don't even mention it. I sure as hell tried not to. Jenny brought it up on that last day. Out of nowhere. She said she wondered how that lady could just keep pluggin' away.

It's the mother child bond, I said to her. Even if your kid's the devil, he's still your kid.

Yeah, she said, but still. That lady was awful strong. She was like, I dunno, like if I was a feminist, she'd be my role model. My queen bee.

What? I said.

She's like a martyr, you know? A feminist martyr.

We broke up pretty soon after that. I made it clear this time. No more fucking around. At least, not on a regular basis.

At work that next day, I quit my job. I decided maybe I'd work as a freelancer. I decided the ninetosixeverybodyelseisdoingitsowhatthehell wasn't for me. Nice and all, just notforme. I decided I'd try out working as a freelancer. That's what people were calling unemployment those days. I mean, if Jenny got by on a freelance wage, I figured I'd be all right.

I spent the next month in my bedroom. For the most part. First I was gettingtogethermyportfolio. Then I was reevaluatingmyportfolio. Then I was buildingmyresume. And for a while I was designingmyportfoliowebsite. Eventually I developed the habit of stealingthingsfromcornerdelis. It was an excuse to leave the apartment. It was something to do.

It started with a pack of gum. I asked Ebrahim for a pack of Kamel Reds, which was a deceit in itself because I had mostly stopped smoking (since I didn't smoke in the house and I never left the house). And as he was reaching for the cigarettes, which were under the counter because even most hipsters weren't dumb enough to smoke Reds, I pocketed a Juicy Fruit.

I felt bad because Ebrahim was a pretty good guy. I smoked the entire pack in my bedroom in about thirty two minutes. It was a hell of an accomplishment and I felt like if I could smoke an entire pack in thirty two minutes, I could probably take my resumeportfoliowebsite and shove it. And then I remembered why I'd smoked the pack to begin with, and it was because of that look on Ebrahim's face after I'd paid. He'd thought I was all right. Might've had to do with me being white. Probably also because he could tell I was a Jew. (I was pretty sure he was Israeli. Actually I was goddamn certain.)

So I went back across the street and asked him for another pack of Kamel Reds. He gave me a funny look, and probably not just because I'd asked him the same thing thirty eight minutes before. Probably more because I must've looked like a total nutjob, having just smoked an entire pack of cigarettes in thirty two minutes. But hell, I was a total nutjob, so I wasn't going to hold it against him. And I slipped the Juicy Fruit back when he wasn't looking.

The next day I asked Ebrahim for another pack of Kamel Reds and received another strange look. I pocketed what I was pretty sure was the exact same Juicy Fruit, paid, and exited. It was exhilarating. And I don't usually use that word. In fact, I looked it up in the dictionary just to make sure it wasn't one of those words people used incorrectly. And it wasn't. I was definitely feeling "very happy, animated, or elated" and as I ran down North 8th Street, towards the water, I decided to hell with diction, sometimes word choice didn't mean shit.

I threw the Juicy Fruit into the East River and watched it sink without any sort of symbolic hesitation. It just sank straight down. And I didn't bother taking the time to check out the skyline—I was much too happy, animated, or elated. Then I headed straight back to H-Q and started to plot my next move. It was around then that I thought about what my mother would tell me if she was still around.

The next few days I stuck to the turf. By the end of the week I'd pocketed Juicy Fruits from every cornerdeli on Bedford from Division Street to Nassau Avenue. That was eleven cornerdelis by my count. That was eleven packs of Juicy Fruit, eleven packs of cigarettes. Needless to say I took up gum chewing and re took up smoking. Needless to say I was getting pretty damned good at the old stickgumpocket. Needless to say by the end of the week I was ready for a new racket.

Needless to say I'd sort of broken my agoraphobic habits and picked up (I looked this one up) kleptomaniac ones. All this time I'd silently wondered to myself whatthefuckisthatguytalkingabout whenever the word was mentioned (in colloquial conversation). Whatthefuckiskelptomania? Needless to say I didn't know then what I know now. Needless to say I was excited because this was finally becoming my story. Not *hers*.

Then there was this night in my apartment. I'd chewed about two packs. At least. I was emptying my wastebasket. Full of gum wrappers. And there was all this stuff at the bottom. Stuck. And it wouldn't come out and I had to scrape it out. But goddamn it wouldn't scrape out, all I had was a pocketknife and it wasn't cutting it. I got the brilliant idea that what I needed was a paint scraper. What I needed was to steal a paint scraper. And then I thought, you know, Juicy Fruit was getting old.

I stole a paint scraper at Home Depot the next day. It was easy. Easier than I expected. Which got me to thinking maybe it's about time I moved on.

As I scraped the gum off the bottom of my wastebasket, I planned my next move. I was planning on really taking authorship now. I was all ready. All for.

Then *she* came back into the story.

She broke up with Jason one day. *She* had just seen "Harold & Maude" and it made *her* cry and *she* realized *she* hadn't cried in years. Maybe not years, but a real long time. So when Jason came home, all *her* stuff was packed up. And *she* didn't really tell Jason *she* was leaving him. *She* did it without saying anything, which was a talent of *hers*. Silence, that is. Killing with silence.

I'm not sure where *she* was crashing, but *she* buzzed into my place emptyhanded telling me about "Harold & Maude," so I'd assumed maybe *she* just needed to vent and maybe *she* was staying with a friend.

But then *she* took me right to bed. Which was fine with me, even though I'd hardly remembered where the button on my pants was. And in the morning *she* asked me what was up with all the Juicy Fruit and I told *her* I was trying to quit smoking.

Then why in hell are there dozens of empty packs of cigarettes everywhere and two ashtrays that say you haven't slept in days?

Well probably, I said, because I haven't slept in days.

We got to talking about life, which tended to be what most of my conversations were about those days despite not liking it very much.

Life is no walk in the park, *she* said to me. Life is a walk in the fucking park, *she* continued. You could take your chances with me. It's not a very good bet, but it's a bet that can be made.

I didn't look at *her* and changed the subject. I asked *her* if *she'd* read "Catcher in the Rye" and *she* had. Well, I said, do you think the kid who borrowed Holden's sweater knew he was going to die in it?

She didn't and *she* said so. *She* started telling me a story about a homeless woman but it got overstuffed in the middle and *she* gave up telling it. The moral, *she* said, was supposed to be how really really wanting something makes getting it way better. But not getting it way worse. And never underestimate eye contact. And sometimes people just have to forgive each other. Because sometimes you were doing something else that day.

She didn't leave my apartment for the next two days, and neither did I. We hardly talked, and it was not so bad. Actually it was pretty good. But I had that itch on the third day and told *her* I needed some more gum, I'd be right back.

She was gone when I got back. I figured *she'd* be back. And even if not that day, then the next, or the next, or sometime anyways. Somewhere down the line.

I played it cool and acted like I was happy to reclaim my story. Happy *she* was out of the picture for now. I figured it was probably the Holden Caulfield comment that helped me reclaim my story.

I wonder what would happen if I robbed a bank, I thought as I stared at a blank ream of paper in my typewriter. I'd picked up the typewriter, years back, only partially because it seemed cool and I kinda wanted to be that person that owned a typewriter. I swore to myself, though, that it was a necessity because I needed a third method to my madness. Staring at the blank computer screen had hurt my eyes and staring at those red lines of notebook paper hurt other places. So the typewriter was that supposed refuge for computerhandwritingwriter'sblock.

And I started to type:

I WONDER WHAT WOULD HAPPEN IF I ROBBED A BANK

And I thought, well, I thought that I couldn't possibly write it unless I'd lived it. At least a little.

And then I thought it had at last become my story.

I got a phone call that night as I started laying the foundation. Punching those keys. I don't know if there's anything more satisfying to an agoraphobic than forcing the keys of a manual typewriter into the floor. And I didn't want to answer the telephone. I could feel myself sinking, sinking into the hole I was forcing into the bottom of my apartment. Pretty soon I'd be able to see my below neighbors, the ones that sometimes fought in Polish and then had really loud sex. It was right out of a New Yorker short story. Or a cheesy action film.

And that damn phone kept ringing. For three hours, maybe more. Finally there was a pause, which threw off my rhythm. Trying to figure out where that sound had gone, half realizing the ring hadn't been the sound of the typewriter carriage needing to be reset.

I lost it there and I was pissed so I chewed a pack of Juicy Fruit. I chewed another pack. I was chewing them four or five pieces at a time and I'd probably needed to see a dentist soon. Then the phone rang again.

I answered it without thinking. Without remembering a few hours earlier. Hello? I said.

What? I said.

What? I said.

No no. I heard you, I said. Just. Just lemme think about this for a second, would ya?

From there I hung up the phone and went to the emergency room.

Man was she looking awful. Jenny had got hit by a car. Which threw a bone in our nomorefuckingaround bit. I'd sort of been avoiding her. Or I guess I'd probably definitely been avoiding her. And as I looked at her sleeping on the bed, the detective half of my brain did some concluding. Two conclusions. Number one: Jenny was the one calling me for hours, I didn't know how many hours exactly, it could've been hoursandhours, but who knows. Number two: Jenny's getting hit by a car was no accident.

Those conclusions were never confirmed by outside sources. I wasn't the type to ask and Jenny wasn't the type to tell. I sat with her for three days and nights. Some friends floated in and out. Her father stopped by (her mother had cancer). *She* didn't come but Jason did. Jason didn't talk to me though. I read aloud from a Saul Bellow novel when Jenny got bored. It was one of those epic novels that was about a rich, petty, neurotic, middle-aged writer.

On that fourth day I escorted her out of the hospital. We'd briefly discussed and decided since she didn't want to give her roommate a hard time and I was freelancing, I'd take care of her for an undecidedamountoftime. Strange coincidence was, as we walked through the lobby, we walked right into *her*.

Wow Jenny, you know, *she* said, I just found out today. Jason didn't tell me until just today, said you'd probably be checking out soon. I'm sorry, I would've been here in a heart beat, kid.

She looked pretty bad herself. I was wondering where *she'd* got that black eye but I didn't really want to know. I didn't want to know where those few pounds had disappeared to either, at *her* weight.

It's fine, it's fine, Jenny responded. Jenny was in a wheelchair. *She* leaned over and hugged Jenny. It was a strange sight. It sort of looked like the two had got into a crackmoneyfight and here they were making up in the hospital lobby. At least, that's the looks we were getting. The crackmoneyfight looks.

I'd ordered a special handicap cab and we all talked as we waited on the curb. I was getting worked up, having been out of my apartment too long.

She said *she'd* never imagined something like this could happen. I can't believe it, *she* said over and over. I can't believe a car hit you. I mean, damn, those cars on Bedford are goddamn centurions. Goddamn centurions. It was on Bedford, I bet, wasn't it.

Jenny nodded. Unless it was an inside thing, I don't think either of us knew what in hell centurions had to do with anything. Right then I started wondering what in hell I ever saw in *her* inthefirstplace. Honest. I couldn't see what had attracted me to the girl, who was clearly at least partially insane.

(Later I remembered that I too was at least partially insane. Later I thought that maybe if I lit a few candles and placed them on the floor instead of somewhere more logical like a tabletop, then maybe I'd be able to see only the important things. Not be distracted. Not by gettingtogethermyportfolio or reevaluatingmyportfolio or designingmyportfoliowebsite or even computerhandwritingwriter'sblock. And maybe if I was lucky, maybe I wasn't as lost as what I'd thought out of the corner of my eye.)

For three weeks, Jenny lived with me. I only left the house to rent movies and get takeout (and sometimes I was stealingthingsfromcornderdelis but my kleptomania was fading fast). I learned to cook a little. I cleaned. I figured her immune system or something, you know, was probably not strong enough for the filth I was slowing into. I took care of her. I had very specific instructions from the doctors that I followed specifically. And we went for checkups every few days.

I had it under control. And I felt in control. It wasn't so bad really—we both had a hell of a recuperation. It was a real homerun because Jenny said maybe five words the entire time. I did the talking. At first she was too weak, but later I suspected maybe she'd learned to listen. I did so much talking I probably couldn't remember half the things I talked about. Mostly it was just boring jibber jabber jibberjabber. But you know, in the state I'd been in those months, I guess I'd forgot how to make it all look like I was doing all right, doing okay.

When I was renting a movie one night (Jenny wanted an action thing), I ran into *her*. I didn't know what to say, really. I hadn't talked to anyone besides Jenny in ages and before that nobody at all. And like I said, I'd lost my ability to make it look like I was all right. So I just stood there, looking at *her*.

Hey, *she* said.

It's been a while, *she* said after I'd said nothing. How's Jenny doing?

I didn't respond again and *she* looked around. The rental store was empty except for an NYU student behind the counter and an overthehill hipster looking at the staff selections. *She* began.

You don't love me anymore, do you?

At first I didn't respond. Then I said, Well, well I don't know. Did I ever love you?

I don't know. Did you?

I paused, avoided looking at *her*, remembering what *she'd* told me about eye contact. About how you can never underestimate it. I looked at the door, then responded: I don't know. I don't even know what love is.

What do you mean you don't know what love is? That's the stupidest thing—I've ever heard.

I grabbed something from the Clint Eastwood section and got out of there with as much tact as I could carry in my pockets.

I walked down Bedford and didn't look back. *She* caught up with me after only a minute.

She said, I know what it's like to be dead. I know what it is to be sad.

I said, Who put all those words in your head? You're making me feel like I'll never belong.

She said, You don't understand what I've said.

I said, Nonono, you're wrong. When I was a boy, everything was right.

I said, Even though you know what you know, I know that I'm ready to leave. Because you're making me feel like I'll never belong.

She said, You don't understand what I've said.

I said, Nonono, you're wrong. When I was a boy, everything was right. Everything was right.

That was it. I didn't realize that *she* had such a grasp on Beatles' lyrics (and that I didn't). I ran off down Bedford. And as I ran I thought, Here's this guy, a total product of the hipsterisms that he hates, all of a sudden resorting to bank robbery to pump a little meaning out of life, which of course he could never get away with, the idea being that he watched Bonnie & Clyde onetoomanytimes (orsomethinglikethat).

And then I thought, Well, what is it with the rules of narrative anyways? What is a resolution? Isn't it really just the idea that you should lose interest in the protagonist, in the conflict, in the story? I don't wanna do that. This is my story. Not *hers*.

BOYFRIEND

KEVIN SAMPSELL

You have a boyfriend now but in 6th grade you said I could hold your hand under the table in Home Ec class. My fingers explored your fingers like they had never felt something so small and delicate before. The palm of your hand was always sweaty and warm.

You have a boyfriend now but we used to go out to lunch together in high school, walking across that empty lot full of weeds to get to Osco, where we would buy Jo-Jos and deli burritos and I would try to sneak as many looks at your breasts as possible. They were too big for your body and one time you complained about them and cried.

You have a boyfriend now but you were the one who made me really want to have a girlfriend in 10th grade. We sat next to each other in a classroom I can surprisingly still picture so clearly and you said I was cute but you were obsessed with Duran Duran and you had braces but you always smiled anyway. I can't remember if you had a pink Karmann Ghia or if you just talked about wanting one, but I always picture you driving one through the student parking lot because I think you were spoiled.

You have a boyfriend now but you told me a couple of years ago that you had a crush on me in middle school when no one knew you were gay. You spent the night at my place a few times and one night we made ourselves stay up all night and walked around town, laughing at our own dumb jokes. We played one-on-one basketball in the park, in the dark. The next morning, a Saturday, we went to our favorite teacher's house and woke her up and she answered the door in her bathrobe and then took us to Osco and bought us food for breakfast. She said we were two of her favorites.

You have a boyfriend now but we used to talk on the phone all the time in 8th grade and almost every sentence started with, "What if…" as in "What if we were locked in the mall all night, where would we go first and what would we eat?" We said to each other, "I like you a lot" and "We should pretend to be a couple at school" and "Let's always be friends, okay?"

You have a boyfriend now but when I was twenty-one and lived in Seattle, you worked at Peaches record store and I think I liked you because you were the only person I know who liked Robyn Hitchcock.

You have a boyfriend now but I always thought it was cool how you would wear your dad's old dress jackets and roll the sleeves up past your elbows and you let me borrow one once before senior prom but I was too embarrassed to wear it because I didn't want to stand out, wasn't ready to stand out. I just wanted to blend in, so I rented a suit and it was white with a burgundy cummerbund and tie and I still felt like I stood out too much.

You have a boyfriend now but you were my friend's girlfriend when we were nineteen and you two were always fighting and one night, when I dropped you off at your apartment, we made out in my car and I never told anyone about it, and we never did anything, but I think we both wanted to.

You have a boyfriend now but we had one night together when I was twenty-five and you came over to my apartment unannounced and said, "Do you want me to come in?" and then I eagerly and nervously took your clothes off. I was eager because you had the largest, most teasingly beautiful breasts of all my friends and I was nervous because I knew you usually dated the big bouncer at the bar I always went to. You were laughing as we undressed and you were laughing as we had sex and you were laughing when I ran out of breath and I wasn't sure if the laughing was a good thing or not.

You have a boyfriend now but you used to ride your bike around my neighborhood in 2001 and I always wanted to talk to you but I never knew your name and I thought you might be kind of famous, like you were in a local band or something. I was outside looking at the still blue sky on September 11th and you rode by with tears in your eyes and I wanted to tell you to stop and talk to me. I wanted you to look at me. I wanted to see if I could help you. I never saw you after that.

You have a boyfriend now but when you were seventeen and I was twenty-two, we used to hang out in Riverfront Park in Spokane and we always went to the arcade there and play video games all afternoon and I thought you were kind of frail and sensitive and supermodel sexy, but just a little too young. We went to your parents' house and watched the TV show, *Doogie Howser, M.D.* because I liked it but you didn't seem impressed with Neil Patrick Harris's character and I don't think you really enjoyed it. At the end of the show, when Doogie types in his journal about the lesson he learned, you laughed at how sappy it was.

You have a boyfriend now but you used to be devoted to me, even though you made fun of me for liking the color brown and never reading books when I was twenty-one. You have a husband now and you had two boys and you told me that you live in the country somewhere and let the kids run free, even though they're under ten. You have a husband now and you told me that he sliced up all your clothes when you had a fight once. You have an ex-husband now and you listen to movie soundtrack music and you sometimes have sex on the first date, even when you don't think it'll be good. You have a boyfriend there and a boyfriend there and an ex-husband at that bar and your next husband in that office building. And other kinds of boys all over, so much so that your devotion to me is hardly there any more. I was the love of your heart, you say, but not of your life.

HE OPENS DOORS, HE CLOSES THEM

KATHLEEN HELLEN

Ladies first, they always said. He feels like he's in high school. The boys surrendered chairs. A white agenda. They paid for dates. There was a popular cologne by Faberge in green-glass bottles, football games. A dry champagne for weddings and anointings of the king. The patriarch of rich plantations. He watches as she sips her lemonade, as if she graced a white veranda. No doubt his swagger is a cop, is criminal. His finger triggers on the winning like the spoils he has driven. To capture or embrace the narrow of her waist. Defend her honor. A patriot. A player. He wants her to feel safe. The single operation of his arm commands her gender.

AN INTERVIEW WITH MICHAEL MARTONE

MATTHEW BAKER

Depending on whom you ask, Michael Martone is either contemporary literature's most notorious prankster, innovator, or mutineer. In 1997 his AAP membership was briefly revoked after Martone published his first two books—a "prose" collection titled *Alive and Dead in Indiana* and a "poetry" collection titled *Double-Wide*—which, aside from *Double-Wide*'s line breaks, were word-for-word identical. His membership to the South African Writers Union was revoked in 1999 after SAWU discovered that, while Martone's registered nom de plume had been "born" in Cape Town, Martone himself had never even been to South Africa. His AWP membership was revoked in 2007, reinstated in 2008, and revoked again in 2011.

After his first two collections, Martone went on to write *Michael Martone*, a collection of fictional contributor's notes originally published among nonfictional contributor's notes in cooperative journals, *The Blue Guide to Indiana*, a collection of travel articles reviewing fictional attractions such as the Memorial to the Fallen Autoworkers of the 1963 Studebaker Bankruptcy (most of which were, again, originally published as nonfiction), a collection of fictional interviews with his mentor Padgett Powell, fictional advertisements in the margins of magazines such as *Hayden's Ferry Review* and *Nashville Review*, poems under the names of nonfictional colleagues, and blurbs for nonexistent books.

But his latest book is perhaps the most revealing—*Racing in Place* is a collection of essays on Martone's obsession with blimps, basketball, and the Indianapolis 500, symbols for him of "this kind of frenetic motion and also this kind of staticness in the Midwest." Born in Fort Wayne, Indiana, Martone has often been described as a regionalist, and his relationship with the Midwest mirrors his relationship with literature: Martone thinks of the Midwest as a "strange, imaginary place, with no distinct borders or boundaries."

Martone now lives in Tuscaloosa, where he teaches in the MFA program at the University of Alabama. In December 2010, Martone's twin sister, P. M. Martone, a concert pianist and spare-time cabinetmaker, had a brain aneurysm in Martone's (Michael's) driveway, and has since been in a coma. When Martone agreed to be interviewed, he explained that he now spends nearly all of his time at Tuscaloosa's Bryce Hospital, where his sister is being cared for, and that our interview would have to be conducted there.

P. M.'s room at Bryce Hospital was sunny and chemical-smelling and wallpapered with cards from Martone's (Michael's) children and grandchildren—P. M. herself is unmarried. Martone offered me a chair at P. M.'s side, next to his own chair, where we sat for the course of the interview; he wore a thick yellow tie that matched almost exactly the shade of P. M.'s hospital gown. Martone had his iPhone plugged into the room's speakers, over which played, on repeat, at low volume, Rachmaninoff's Op. 29. "I don't know if she can hear it," Martone said, "but it was her favorite piece—I'm hoping to lure her back with it." During most the interview, Martone held P. M.'s hand.

I should also note that I began the interview with a question that, among interviewers, Martone is notorious for dodging—that question being just when and why, exactly, Martone began writing—and Martone surprised me by actually answering. After the interview, when I asked Martone why he hadn't simply, as usual, asked for the next question, Martone said only, "P. M. was in love with a boy once, and you sort of remind me of him."

Just when and why, exactly, did you begin writing?

I never wanted to be a writer, I never wanted to write short stories, or poems, or fictional advertisements. What I wanted, as a teenager, and even in my early twenties, was to compose the soundtracks for videogames. I was obsessed with the classic Nintendo canon, particularly those games with a narrative bent: *The Legend of Zelda*, *Mario Bros.*, *Final Fantasy*. My friends, the Jelusos, these cousins who lived in our cul-de-sac, they hacked my NES console, and then they tinkered with the games' designs while I tinkered with the games' music. We played *D&D*, *Dungeons & Dragons*, seven days a week as high schoolers—I was our group's GM—the Jelusos and I had this idea that *D&D* experience, the experience of creating these impromptu game-type fictions for a number of "players," might somehow someday translate into jobs at Nintendo Co.

The Jelusos, they wanted to be the next Shigeru Miyamoto (or Miyamotos): they saw him as the master of their craft. Miyamoto had written and designed *Donkey Kong*, *Mario Bros.*, *Kid Icarus*, *The Legend of Zelda*. The Jelusos had read an article in a gaming magazine about Miyamoto, as a child—about how nine-year-old Miyamoto had been roaming around in the woods behind his house in Sonobe and had come across a hole in the ground—a cave. The next day Miyamoto came back with a lantern, and he ended up spending most of his childhood afternoons in this cave, exploring its passageways. Which—as this origin story seems to suggest that this experience was Miyamoto's formative one, that this cave obviously must have served as some inspiration for both *Mario Bros.* and *The Legend of Zelda*—the article said that this cave had become a sort of shrine for gamers: gamers from the United States, from Europe, from Australia, they were making pilgrimages to Sonobe to look for this cave. That was the thing—nobody knew where the cave was, exactly. Sonobe has a number of larger caves that had been open to tourists for years, but they were far too large to be the cave Miyamoto had described.

Incidentally, a number of artists have described having similar experiences. In *Blankets*, for example, Craig Thompson talks about how one day he and his brother, when they were children, found this hole in the ground—Thompson's experience was, the first day they found it, the cave was large enough for him and his brother to hunch down and crawl into it, large enough that they saw salamanders as they went deeper into the cave; on the second day they came back, and then the hole was only large enough for Thompson and his brother to stick their heads into it, and they couldn't see any salamanders, it didn't even seem to be that deep of a cave at all; and on the third day, the hole in the ground had disappeared.

Others—Banksy, David Bowie, Ts'ui Pên—they've described having this same hole-in-the-ground experience.

Isn't Ts'ui Pên a character from one of Borges' stories?

Ts'ui Pên is, yes, a fictional writer from Borges' "The Garden of Forking Paths," but Ts'ui Pên is also the pseudonym used by an Italian (allegedly) writer. Pên has written one novel, *The Numberless*, of which Pên rather infamously published only a single copy. It circulates by hand—one person reads it, then gives it to somebody else, and then that person reads it, and so on.

Nobody's thought to photocopy the novel and put a few more copies into circulation?

The nature of the novel makes it more or less impossible to photocopy.

You've seen it?

Yes—as an undergraduate I was at one of the few public readings Thomas Pynchon ever gave, and afterward I asked sort of an asshole-type question, which Pynchon ignored, refused to answer, as he should have. But afterward, at the reading's reception, Pynchon approached me with the book. "Maybe this will answer your question," he said, and then he took a biscuit from my plate, and then he walked away. Chewing my biscuit.

I didn't realize what it was, exactly, until I had brought the book back to my apartment, which I shared with my now-wife, then-fiancée. "Ts'ui Pên!" she said when she saw it. "M, do you know what this is?" In those days she called me M. Now she refers to me as Sting, for reasons I probably shouldn't say.

Whom did you give the novel to, once you were finished?

Well my wife stole it from me before I'd made it past even the title page, so how it circulated was this: Pynchon gave it to me, it was stolen from me by my then-fiancée, which then-fiancée then gave it back to me (at which point she was then my wife), and then I read it, and I finished it that December, and then I gave it to our mail carrier for Christmas.

Your mail carrier?

It was our first house, she was our first mail carrier, I thought she deserved something special.

Nobody knows the identity of Ts'ui Pên?

Like Banksy's, Ts'ui Pên's identity remains unknown.

So you wanted to write the soundtracks for videogames.

Yes—so the Jelusos wanted to be Miyamotos, but I wanted to be the next Nobuo Uematsu, the next Koji Kondo. I saw them as the masters of their craft: Uematsu had scored the soundtracks for the *Final Fantasy* canon, Kondo for the *Mario Bros.* and *The Legend of Zelda*.

By the time I graduated high school in 1988, the Jelusos had succumbed, career-wise, to various vices: Sal to methamphetamines, Michael to cocaine, Anthony to rollerblading. They'd forgotten about their Miyamoto fantasies entirely.

But I'd taken three semesters of Japanese. And so with my baseball-stadium savings—as teenagers my sister and I worked at a popcorn stand in Indiana Wesleyan University's baseball stadium—I bought a one-way ticket to Kyoto. I had some songs I'd been working on, and I wanted to meet Uematsu and Kondo, I wanted them to tell me what they thought.

You were just going to walk into Nintendo's building?

Uematsu didn't work for Nintendo Co., Uematsu worked for Square. I respected Kondo's work, but Uematsu is who I was really after. I wanted Uematsu as my guru.

However, Uematsu's reputation was one of being even more absurdly hermetic than even Miyamoto himself. So my plan was to, yes, walk into Nintendo Co.'s building, and somehow acquire Uematsu's phone number or address from someone at Nintendo. After which I thought I'd pop into Kondo's office, or studio, or wherever he did his scoring, and at least say hello.

Incidentally, for whatever reason I had brought along my social security card—I wasn't entirely clear on what exactly you did or did not need, when traveling to another country, and somehow I had come under the impression that along with a passport I'd need my SSC—which SSC I then proceeded to lose somewhere in Kyoto's subway system during my first night there. This resulted in my becoming probably one of the earliest victims of identity theft.

Someone had stolen your social security card?

This man, Toru something, stole my social security number and used it to open a number of American credit cards and then basically just started an entirely new life. He started living, quite extravagantly, as Michael Martone, in downtown Tokyo.

I didn't find any of this out until years later, though, when the financial damage this Michael, this Toru had done, was almost irreparable.

It was that experience, though, with Michael/Toru, that inspired me to take identity theft to literature: the fictional interviews with Powell, the poems by "Neal Bowers," and so on.

So that's the when and why? You began writing because of the incident with the identity thief?

No no no, I'm still answering that question. I'd been writing for almost a year already when I discovered that my identity had been stolen. And at this point—in Kyoto—I still planned on being a writer, not of fictions, but of videogame soundtracks.

So I should just get to the point, which is that I never met Nobuo Uematsu, I never met Koji Kondi, I failed to ever even locate Nintendo Co.'s building. Like the Jelusos, I succumbed, career-wise, to a vice: mine was Naoko Kasahara.

The morning after I lost my SSC, I was wandering around sort of the general vicinity of where I thought Nintendo Co.'s building was supposed to be, when I saw a sign in the window of this department store-sized arcade; the sign said Shigeru Miyamoto, Miyamoto himself, was giving a signing that afternoon.

The line for Miyamoto—Miyamoto wasn't even there yet—had already spilled from the arcade's fifth floor down to its fourth, its third, its second, its first, and then out the arcade's front doors and around the block. A lot of Japanese kids, with NES cartridges for Miyamoto to sign, but also a number of backpacker-looking Americans and Europeans, whom I took to be among those same pilgrims who came for Miyamoto's cave.

I got in line, stood there all day, never met Miyamoto—the signing ended before I'd even made it into the building—and met a woman in line named Naoko, who I proceeded to, in a naïve, cliché, teenager sort of way, fall wildly in love with almost immediately.

After a day, a week, a month, I'd forgotten about Uematsu altogether. I got a job in a kitchen, frying tempura six nights a week, and moved in with Naoko.

Were you still in touch with your family, your sister, at this point?

I wrote them a letter, which I later found out took nearly seven months to actually arrive—the letter just barely beat me back.

This was before email, of course, and before Michael Martone had the sort of funds necessary to make an international call. The *other* Michael Martone—Michael/Toru, now living in Tokyo—he had the funds, but of course we weren't in touch.

And P. M. had left, too; we'd bought our plane tickets together. Mine for Kyoto, P. M.'s for Lanai. P. M. was working on a pineapple plantation that summer, with one of her best friends, and I was much closer with P. M. than I was with our parents, so at this point I didn't really feel much of a need to be "in touch" with Fort Wayne.

Anyway, I was in Kyoto, and working, illegally, in a tempura kitchen—I was an illegal immigrant. And I was living with Naoko, who kept bits of colored cloth knotted into her hair, and whose lips were always dry to the point of being marked with purplish streaks, and who stood, Naoko, just barely five feet tall.

Naoko was a student at Shuchiin University, where her father taught economics, and her father was not entirely thrilled to find that his daughter was dating an illegal immigrant, but also Naoko was, to a certain extent, rather disturbed, so at the same time I think her father was just sort of relieved to have someone else taking care of her.

It was the tiniest things that would unravel her, Naoko; we subscribed to the local newspaper, for example, and one night before I left for work I brought the newspaper in and Naoko began flipping through it and she found that, in our newspaper, on the page with the obituaries, someone had clipped one of the obituaries right out, as if with a pair of scissors.

Which, I offered Naoko what I thought were several reasonable theories about how this could have happened—for instance, that maybe our newspaper deliverer couldn't afford his own newspaper subscription, but that a loved one of his had died, and so that then he had clipped the obituary of his loved one from our newspaper, as he knew we wouldn't need it. Or maybe, I thought, the newspaper publisher had printed the obituary of a missing person who had been missing for so long that they had now been assumed dead, but shortly after the newspaper was printed, that missing person had been discovered to be alive, and so the publisher had had the obituary clipped from the newspapers rather than pay for an entire reprinting.

But Naoko became obsessed with it. She was sure that someone had done this to our newspaper, and our newspaper alone, intentionally. She thought that the person who'd died must have been someone she'd known, and that someone was trying to hide this death from her. She made me run to the newspaper stand at the end of the block, which I did, but of course it was the evening, the stand was empty, sold out, which Naoko took only as a sign that her theory was correct, that someone was conspiring to keep this death from her.

Incidentally, around this time there was a rumor going around Shimogyo Ward, the neighborhood we lived in, that a multinational company based there in Kyoto had been paying local graveyards for the bodies of their dead; the story was that this multinational company had a number of unmarked sweatshops in Shimogyo where they reanimated these dead bodies, brought them back to life to do unpaid labor for the company—assembling electronics, sewing sweaters, etc.—until the bodies would deteriorate to the point where they could no longer function. Then the multinational would buy another batch of bodies, to replace those that had simply fallen apart.

Paul French lived in an apartment just a few blocks from ours, and he claimed he had actually met one of these sweatshop undead; this man had escaped the sweatshop to make amends with his wife and his son, French said, but as the man's body deteriorated, so did his brain, and with it his memories—at the point when French met him, the man could not remember where his wife and son lived, or even their names, or even his own name, only that before he had been killed in a subway accident, that the man had somehow hurt or abused his wife and son, and that he had been brought back for a reason, to find them again, to tell them he was sorry—but of course now the man could not find them.

Is this the poet Paul French, who told you this story?

He was wildly popular in Japan, at that time, which is why he ended up moving to Utah, where still nobody has ever heard of him.

French was of the opinion that a work of literature had more value, more meaning, the fewer the people that have read it. Some of his poems, after he'd written them, he'd walk them over to our apartment, and he'd read them to Naoko—I wasn't allowed to listen, I had to sit out on the balcony—and after he'd read them, he'd burn them over our stove, so that the poems would be his and Naoko's alone. French was constantly setting off our fire alarm.

For some of his poems, even, French kept it to a readership of one. French was known for writing on this one bridge in Kyoto—the Shichijo Ohashi Bridge, I think—for writing poems onto this pad of paper as he was walking, and then, when he'd finished a poem, and reread it once or twice, for then tearing the poem from his notepad and flinging it over the bridge and into the river. Well, Kyoto's French enthusiasts caught on to this fairly quickly. They started following him on these walks—it wasn't a very large bridge, or a very deep river, and when French would toss one of his poems over his shoulder and into the river, his fanatics would go leaping in—sometimes they'd already be underneath the bridge, waiting—after the poems.

You personally never met any of the sweatshop undead?

Or here's another example of how Naoko was unwell. When Naoko was younger, she'd taken a trip with her school to a local museum. And one of her classmates noticed the elevator's weight limit—it was 1,000 kilograms, Naoko said, so about 2,200 pounds—and convinced them all to test it.

So they all met at the fifth floor, the top floor—where, Naoko said, they thought they would be least likely to encounter any of their teachers—and then crammed in about thirty of her classmates. Naoko said some kids were on other kids' shoulders, they were packed in that tight. Naoko was shoved up against the elevator's buttons, so close, she said, that it was like she was trying to look through them.

Then the ringleader, from the back corner of the elevator, called out for Naoko to take them down, and so Naoko nosed the button for the second floor, which lit up, and the elevator's doors closed and the elevator shook and then groaned and then crawled down about half a floor before it stopped and the lights shut off.

Well, they'd proven the elevator did have its limits.

They were trapped in the elevator for nearly an hour. But of course they thought they'd never get out, so that hour felt more like an infinity. Naoko said that within seconds, half of the kids were peeing, and the other half of the kids were crying because they could feel the pee sopping through the peeing kids' clothes into their own. Then came the vomiting, the groping, the elbowing, the shrieking.

A boy next to Naoko, at some point during all of this, that boy's wrist was broken.

…

So one thing Naoko liked to do was she liked to go to this multinational company near our apartment—not the multinational rumored to keep sweatshop undead, I don't think—this fifty-floor glass building, in the center of which was a glass elevator: glass walls, a glass floor. The only part of the elevator you couldn't see through was its buttons—sixty black metal buttons (fifty for the floors, then ten various basement- and roof- and emergency-related buttons)—and the steel frame of it.

On days she didn't have class, Naoko would sometimes spend all day in the elevator, riding it up and down and up again, watching the numbers light up and go dark, riding it until the building closed.

She said it was her way of being strong, of showing herself that she wasn't afraid of what had happened to her anymore, but I thought her thing with the elevator was frankly sort of unhealthy.

What I wanted to do was I wanted to help her. I wanted to make her whole again, unneuroticize her various neuroses, make her believe I wasn't going to leave her. Because I wasn't. She was my number one favorite human I'd ever met, the thoughts in her brain were always the funniest or cutest or most brilliant thoughts I'd ever imagined, she had perfect lips, I wanted to spend every day with her until the two of us died, and even then I wanted the evil and probably fictional multinational company to bring us back again so that Naoko and I could do unpaid sweatshop labor but still in that way be together.

But Naoko was possessed by the idea that I would leave her, that I didn't love her because I *couldn't* love her, that it was impossible for anyone to actually love her, herself, as she saw herself. Which was only reinforced when she visited a fortuneteller in Kamigyo Ward, which fortuneteller told Naoko that it would end poorly between us, that I would come to hurt her. Which was only reinforced all the more when Naoko went to another Kamigyo-Ward fortuneteller, looking for some sort of counter fortune, which second fortuneteller told Naoko that I was not human, not fully, that I had no "self," that "the boy that you love, something killed his identity before he was born."

And so began my war with Kyoto's fortunetellers.

Were you feeling homesick for the States, through all of this? I mean, you had never planned on staying in Kyoto this long, at least not when you first came.

I never felt homesick. I don't think I could have felt homesick, the way that I lived.

P. M. and I were in Paris a year or two ago, browsing through the antique books at Shakespeare and Co., when in a 17th-century almanac P. M. found this anecdote about Finnish sailors: it seems that when Finnish sailors were far from Finland—sailing along the coast of Thailand, or around the tip of South Africa, or wherever—and they began showing symptoms of homesickness, that the nonhomesick sailors would take the homesick sailors into the longboat, and row them onto shore, and then *bury the homesick sailors alive*, up to their necks.

It was supposed to be a cure for nostalgia. The thought was, if you bury a homesick sailor in the sand here—if you bury him *to his neck* in this new place—he'll forget where he came from, become immersed in this new land.

More holes in the ground.

The same reason we bury our dead—we want them to forget where they came from, to move on, not to haunt the rooms where we're still living.

And that was how I lived, in Kyoto. Culturally, linguistically, sexually, gastronomically, I'd buried myself to my neck in it. It's not that I didn't want to leave—I'd forgotten there were other places where I had ever even belonged.

Naoko was bothered, deeply bothered, by the fortunes these fortunetellers had given her. She spent three or four days in the glass building, riding the elevator, coming back to me only once the building had closed. While she rode the elevator, I thought about the fortunes: I didn't believe in magic, I didn't believe in fortunetelling, but at some point I realized that these fortunetellers did have some power—they had not *seen* some truth about the future, but rather, because Naoko was someone who believed in what they said, the fortunetellers had *made* a truth about the future simply by saying it.

Like I said, I didn't believe in any of it, but I knew that Naoko *did*. And I realized that I could fight these fortunetellers with my own magic—that I could make Naoko believe in certain truths about our future in the same way that the fortunetellers had.

But I was on my own. French had holed up, was basically gone, was working with a number of other expat writers on what would eventually become *The Butcher's Ennui*.

That's the novel written by six or seven different writers?

Right. Although it's never indicated, in the novel, which writer wrote which sections of it. In a novel like *The Disastrous Tale of Vera and Linus*, Ball and Bjornsdottir use a numbering system to indicate which sections Ball wrote and which sections Bjornsdottir. Or in this interview, even, which is being "written" in a sense by two different writers—you and me—it's made clear to the reader which words you've put onto the page and which words I have. But in *The Butcher's Ennui*, nobody knows. I've always assumed that French was recruited to write Elizabeth Klemm's sections. Klemm is a poet in the novel—her sections often move back and forth between prose and poetry.

Anyway, French was more or less my only friend in Kyoto, aside from Naoko, and he had holed up working on *The Butcher's Ennui*. So I was on my own.

What I did, for my first spell, was I walked to a local fish market, where they also sold Daruma dolls. I bought a Daruma doll, and then I walked to French's apartment and begged French to please open the door and promised I wasn't going to stay or bother him and then when he opened the door begged him for a tube of black paint, and then once I had the black paint took it and the Daruma doll back to—

Daruma doll?

It's this hollow, sort of roundish doll they make in Japan. A Zen doll. They're sold with only the whites of their eyes—you buy the dolls blind.

What you're supposed to do is, you paint one of its eyes and then you make a wish: you ask the doll for something, like a genie. With its one eye, the doll does its magic for you. Then, once the doll has performed its task, you paint in its other eye, as a reward.

So I gave my Daruma an eye, and then I told it to erase the fortuneteller's fortunes, to rewrite them with its own magic. When Naoko came home from the elevator, I showed her the doll and told her what I had asked it to do. She jumped on my back and kissed my neck and told me we should keep the doll on the shelf above our bed until the time had come to paint its other eye.

So it had worked.

Well, it worked for about an afternoon.

While I was away that night, working in the tempura kitchen, Naoko was rooting through my backpack—I was surprised she hadn't done this before; Naoko was sort of unabashedly nosy—and found the comics books I'd brought from the States. I'd brought them to read on the plane. And one of them was this DC comic, *Cancer*, whose print run was maybe three to four issues tops, and which was about a superhero who was basically this anthropomorphic crab who's the personification of the zodiac sign of Cancer. At the back of each issue they'd include a zodiac chart—complete, not only with the various zodiac signs, but also with each sign's compatibilities *and incompatibilities.*

So Naoko found the chart, and discovered that I was a Gemini, which was supposed to be (according to this DC comic) notoriously incompatible with her own sign, Pisces.

So then she was distraught again.

So back to the doll market.

No, I knew I'd need new spells—I couldn't just buy a 500-yen Daruma doll every time Naoko became emotionally distressed over one of her superstitions.

One of the other cooks at the tempura kitchen was this pouch-cheeked, thick-wrinkled, ninety-something Chinese man named Xueqin, who, like me, was an illegal immigrant. Xueqin was the one who helped me counter this Western-zodiac magic—he taught me about the Chinese zodiac, taught me that by the Chinese system, Naoko had been born in the Year of the Rabbit, and I had been born in the Year of the Dog. According to Chinese-zodiac magic, Xueqin said, Naoko and I were notoriously *compatible.*

It was this quest that I was on, this quest to find magic I didn't believe in to save Naoko from herself, that forced me *out* into Kyoto, out even *beyond* Kyoto—at one point as far as Sapporo—forced me really to become fluent in Japanese, and to meet people, people other than Naoko and French and the other cooks in the kitchen. Before then, Naoko and I had rarely left her apartment. But now I went trekking all over Kyoto, with or without her, bent over the gutters, looking for lucky coins. I wrote P. M. in Lanai, asked her to make a sacrifice to the volcanoes, to ask them for us for luck. I went in search of monks, of astrologers, of the even merely superstitious. I recruited every backpacker-looking American and European and Australian I could find—carpenters, oyster divers, dishwashers, boxers, followers of the cult of Caspod—and wherever they were headed next, made them vow that they would help us. I nailed a list to our bedroom wall, made Naoko read it, made her read the name of each backpacker and the magic they would do for us. Jack Dowland, leaving for Scotland, he would kiss the Blarney Stone for us, reap some of its kissing magic. Kiley Alderink, Bradley Dawson, headed next for Bangladesh, they would trek into the jungle for us, learn what they could of the mystics' magic. Adam Castle, headed to Las Vegas, he swore he would mail us a box crammed to the brim with the feet of rabbits. Douglas McCabe, leaving for India, he would mail us a jar of water from the Ganges, and after India, from an island off the coast of Africa, the quill of a porcupine. Then I instructed everyone, everyone I'd met, the carpenters, the oyster divers, the dishwashers, the boxers, the followers of the cult of Caspod, the purse thieves, the mahjong gamblers, the grave robbers, the bicycle repairmen, the professional mourners, the public restroom managers, the mochi vendors, all of them, ordered all of them, each and every one, to scour their cities for lucky coins, to walk always with a bent head, to search under the docks and the park benches and the tables of the teashops, and then to drop these lucky coins into all of the fountains and the wells and the rivers of the world, to harvest the potent magic of water, a magic, I told Naoko, that covers three-quarters of the world's surface, and that has burrowed its holes into and under nearly all of the rest of it.

…

…

So did it work?

What do you mean, did it work? You mean, did Naoko come to believe that we were destined to be together?

My mistake was the tarot cards.

What tarot cards?

I was trying everything, at this point: I was teaching myself to read tea leaves, teaching myself palm reading, augury, numerology, oneiromancy. While I was in Sapporo, meeting with an astrologer who lived there, I bought a deck of antique tarot cards—Naoko had told me that she knew how to read tarot, and I thought that if she had her own deck, she could read our cards once or twice a day, and that way set her mind at ease.

Naoko loved the deck—it was this 19th-century deck, made in Italy, the cards were all in Italian, with these ornate illustrations—but she refused to use it until we had learned the deck's origin. She needed to know who had owned the deck before her, she said—whether the cards had been used by someone wicked or kind. She didn't want to use them if they were carrying any "negative energy."

So I told her we would trace the origin of the cards. Which is how I ended up, finally, in Sonobe—Shigeru Miyamoto's hometown.

The town with the caves?

That one. I'd called the shop in Sapporo where I'd gotten the cards, and the owner had said he'd bought the cards in an estate sale—this hundred-something mystic from Sonobe had died, and when his children had sold his belongings, most of them had been bought up by this Sapporo antique shop.

That wasn't enough for Naoko, though—she said we needed to go to Sonobe, meet this mystic's children, and ask them what their father had been like.

It seems like that would tell you less about whether the father was wicked or kind than about the children themselves—about their relationship with their father.

The children were all we had—the mystic was dead. So we took a train to Sonobe.

I should mention that the owner of the antique shop had told me, "Don't go to Sonobe—this son who lives there, he is a very unpleasant man." But Naoko insisted that we go.

What we didn't know was that the son—the mystic's son—was the cofounder and leader of CAPGRAS, a group of militant Japanese revolutionaries.

Was CAPGRAS that group behind the sarin gas attacks? On Tokyo's subway system?

No, that was Aum Shinrikyo. That happened much later than any of this. CAPGRAS was, unlike Aum Shinrikyo, not a cult, and, as far as I'm aware, had not killed any civilians—they were militant only against the Japanese government itself, against JGSDF and the Prefectural Police.

When we got to Sonobe, we wandered through town, peeking into teashops and tempura restaurants, asking if anyone knew where we could find Ikiryo or Goma Tamura. We learned rather quickly that Goma Tamura, the mystic's daughter, had "gone away"; when it came to Ikiryo, the mystic's son, nobody would say.

Instead, one of CAPGRAS found us. We were standing outside of a butcher's shop, across the street from a pair of housepainters who were arguing: these housepainters were covered in yellow paint—their coveralls, their boots, their hair, their faces—one of them had a swollen eye, the other a swollen mouth. We were asking a mochi vendor about Goma Tamura.

While we were standing there, a man in black pants and a black jacket approached us—he was wearing a striped headband, and he had light blue eyes, which of course is unusual for a Japanese man. "Ikiryo Tamura?" he said. "I'm not Ikiryo," I said, "I'm looking for Ikiryo." "That's what they said," he said. "Come with me."

We followed the man to a car, and then—I didn't want to get in, but Naoko insisted, "Come on, get in, it will be faster!"—drove us through Sonobe, to what we assumed would be Ikiryo's house. We passed some of the larger caves, where backpackers in backpacks of assorted colors stood in line outside of them, each of them with a fistful of yen, waiting to go inside. We passed another group of housepainters, too, again covered in yellow paint, some of them with bruised faces—instead of arguing, these ones were simply walking along the road, back toward town, from where we'd come. Naoko was carrying the tarot cards. She looked, for once, happy to be outside of our apartment.

"What do you want with Ikiryo?" the man with the striped headband asked, from the front seat where he was driving. "We have his father's tarot cards," Naoko said. "We want to know more about them." The man said, "We're almost there."

When we got to Ikiryo's house, the man with the striped headband, along with a number of other men in striped headbands, tied us to a tree. "What are you doing?" Naoko shouted at them, and after the men in striped headbands had gone into the house, she said, "Michael, why did they tie us to this tree?" "I told you," I said, "not to get into the car."

I remember in the yard of Ikiryo's house, there was a stone birdbath, which a number of children were drinking from. Then a woman, also in a striped headband, came out of the house and chased them away—like birds, the children went tearing off across the yard, weaving back and forth among each other, making silly noises. Some birds, some actual birds, were perched on the edge of a stone well not far from our tree—it seemed like the birds had been waiting for these children to leave, because as soon as the children had disappeared into the trees, the birds flew to the birdbath and took up where the children had left off.

The men in striped headbands came back outside. They were arguing. "Take them to Kawataro," someone said. "His dogs will tell you everything we need to know." "That's not good enough," another said. Then they came over to us. The man with light blue eyes wasn't with them. "How do we know you are who you say you are?" one of them shouted. "Are you with the police? Who sent you here looking for Ikiryo?" "We have his father's tarot cards," Naoko said, "the ones you took from me just now—ask Ikiryo about them." "Ikiryo's father was a weak man," another shouted. "You shouldn't have come here. Who sent you here? Are you with those capitalist demons?" "I'm sorry," I said, "it's just that I'm in love with her, and I go wherever she tells me." Here Naoko kissed me on the cheek, and then they untied us and put us back into the car.

They drove us to a farm down the road. The man with light blue eyes was back and was driving again. At the farm, they took us out of the car and dragged us to a windmill. Kawataro, the farmer, met them there. He wore no headband and looked quite afraid. The men in headbands tied us to the windmill, and then they said something to Kawataro. He nodded, and then he went off behind his house.

Kawataro came back with three dogs, white dogs with bloodshot eyes that looked more like wolves than actual dogs, leashed with leather cords to Kawataro's wrist. The dogs were fighting the leashes, barking and snarling, as Kawataro led them on. The men in striped headbands all stepped back—as far as the car, where they'd parked it—as the dogs approached.

The dogs came over to us, where we were tied, and licked our faces. They sniffed my hair for a while, and Naoko's shoes. Then Kawataro took them away again.

The men in striped headbands dragged us back into the car. "Let me tell you something, you two," the man with light blue eyes said, driving again. "Those dogs are famous in this neighborhood. Those dogs hate old Hatsumi, they hate old Itoh, and they especially hate Ikiryo, and old Hatsumi is the nastiest woman in Sonobe, and old Itoh is a miser and a thief, and Ikiryo beats his horses. Let me tell you, those dogs can smell anything: trickery, corruption, betrayal. Anyone evil or untrustworthy, those dogs do everything they can to tear them to pieces. They'd kill me where I stood, if they could get at me." He pulled the car back into Ikiryo's house. "Those dogs can smell other things too: naivety, weakness, simpleness. People like that, the dogs show them their tongues instead of their teeth." They dragged us out of the car and toward the stone well as the man kept talking. "So if you have those dogs' approval, then you have my approval. Those dogs can smell imbalance, disharmony, something that doesn't belong, from a field away."

Then they sent us into the well.

Into the well?

There was a ladder that went down into it—the well was empty, no water.

The man with light blue eyes went ahead of us, a few of the other men behind us. At the bottom of the well they led us through a door and into an underground room—it looked like a bomb shelter, WWII-era maybe, except it was especially large, and the room smelled like paint.

Paint?

The man with light blue eyes later told us what had happened: Ikiryo had hired a painting company to come paint the underground room; Ikiryo was planning on setting it up as CAPGRAS' new headquarters, and he wanted the room painted black and yellow, CAPGRAS colors, plus one wall painted with the CAPGRAS flag. Anyway, at some point as the men were painting, the paint boss let it slip whose bomb shelter they were painting—he said something about how the shelter belonged to Ikiryo, and about how they weren't just painting the walls, but how they'd also have to paint this flag. Well, then some of the painters became alarmed—if they'd seen Ikiryo's new headquarters, they said, that meant that Ikiryo would have to kill them. The paint boss tried to explain that he and Ikiryo were friends, childhood friends, and that Ikiryo trusted him and his workers, but then the painters started fighting, some of them pro-Ikiryo and most of them anti-, in the room there underground. After they were too tired to keep hitting each other, they collected their paintbrushes, climbed out of the well, and walked back into town—the anti-Ikiryo painters refused to ride with their paint boss, knowing now that he was pro-.

All we saw, though, when they took us in to see Ikiryo, was the aftermath: when they were fighting, the painters had slammed each other against the walls, against the door, leaving handprints and bodyprints where the paint had been wet. It looked as if, all over the room, men made of paint had been peeled from the walls.

Naoko showed Ikiryo the tarot cards, which the man with light blue eyes had given back to her.

"These were my father's," Ikiryo said. Ikiryo wore a striped headband, of course, and the same black pants and black jacket. He had a fat nose, and a tattoo of a crab on his neck under his jaw. He sat on a wooden chair, cleaning a paintbrush in a metal bucket. "I sold them because I never wanted to see them again. So why, then, would you bring them back to me?"

"She just wanted to know what your father was like," I said. "She didn't want to use them if the cards had been used by someone who was wicked."

"My father," Ikiryo said, "was a kind man," and then he spit onto the ground.

"That's all we needed to know," I said, "thank you and goodbye."

The man with the light blue eyes led us toward the door, but as he did, Naoko said over her shoulder, "Your father was a mystic. If he were alive today, I would ask him, should I stay with this man I came with? Will he stay with me forever?"

Ikiryo laughed, and then he said, "Old Ikiryo was not the only Ikiryo with certain powers. I can tell you this much—you can stay with that boy if you want to, but he is not the boy for you. Or rather, you are not the girl for him. His life would be better, if you were gone."

…

…

So then they just let you go?

Of course they let us go. We were just kids, really.

But a week later, after we were back in Kyoto, one night I came home from the tempura kitchen, and Naoko was gone. She'd disappeared—she'd taken everything, even my backpack, my money, my passport—everything but our one-eyed Daruma doll.

Your passport?

She left me nothing, so that I wouldn't have the resources I'd need to follow her.

Why? Because of what Ikiryo had said?

I don't know. Maybe. I think maybe she did listen to Ikiryo—she wasn't paying attention to everything that was happening, she misunderstood the signs.

Misunderstood how?

Ikiryo wasn't a mystic, he wasn't a fortuneteller, he wasn't known for his sixth sense-type insights. But the *dogs* were. Kawataro's dogs. They were *known* for their insights, and when the dogs came to us, they gave us their approval. The man from CAPGRAS, he'd said the dogs could smell "imbalance," could smell "disharmony," but they didn't smell those on us. We were balanced, we had harmony, we could have, I think, been happy. For me, that's what the experience had meant: the tarot cards were safe to use, and we were meant to be together. But for her it had meant something different: the tarot cards were safe to use, but my life would be better if she were gone.

I spent a month living with Xueqin, the Chinese cook, and his wife, still working in the tempura kitchen and trying to find Naoko. On New Year's Day, I walked to a temple near Xueqin's apartment for Daruma Kuyo; on New Year's Day, any Daruma dolls bought throughout the year are brought to one of these temples, and then they're all piled together and set on fire. I put our doll in with the others. I didn't stay to watch it burn.

How long was it before you gave up on Naoko coming back?

Not long after that, Xueqin and his wife put me on a train to Tokyo. From the train station in Tokyo, I walked to the U.S. Embassy, and a couple days later was on a flight back home.

But it did take me—it's taken me—a rather long time to process all of this.

What was that process like?

At first I tried to lose myself in music, in my keyboard, like I'd lost myself before, in videogame soundtracks. But I couldn't really get this new thing out of me in that same way—I found that tones, that notes, these wordless things, that I couldn't really communicate what I was feeling with them.

P. M. was the one who gave me the notebook. She'd brought it back for me from Lanai. "I did what you asked," she said, "with the volcanoes." She'd meant me to write my songs into the notebook, but instead I started writing about what had happened to me, about Naoko, about what it was like for me now that she was gone.

Like French, as soon as I'd finished writing about it, I'd tear the pages out of my notebook and throw them into the trash. I didn't want anyone to see them—I wasn't writing for anyone else, yet. I was writing them for me.

So that's the when and why. I began writing in the winter of 1989, in the basement of my parents' house in Fort Wayne, Indiana, because Naoko was gone, and I wanted some way to bring her back again.

So the stories in Alive and Dead in Indiana, *the poems in* Double-Wide: *in those, Naoko is—*

Yes, that's her. Just with a different name. And in Fort Wayne instead of Kyoto—it was easier to write about it, pretending it had happened in some other place.

Have you ever been back to Kyoto?

Years later, yes, when I was in Tokyo sorting out all of that business with Michael/Toru, my identity thief. While I was in Japan, I decided to take the train back to Kyoto, just to see how it had changed.

I went to our old apartment, Naoko's and mine, but the building now was gone. So was Xueqin's building. Where the tempura kitchen had been, they now sold bubble tea.

The glass building was still there, though. I went inside, when I saw it was still standing—I knew Naoko wouldn't be there, but still I had to look, I had to see with my own eyes that she was gone, that she really, actually, was not in it anymore. I stood in the lobby of the building, at the base of the glass elevator, staring up and up at the balconies of endless floors—it was dusk, and the elevator was lit, a tiny cube of yellow floating there. The elevator was moving up and down, but Naoko was not on it.

GOODY-GOODY

ALICIA ERIAN

I started working part-time at this dry cleaners after school, and the girls who had already been working there for a while showed me how they stole from the till. You could only do it with the customers who paid in exact change. They'd give you their slip, you'd get them their clothes, then you'd take their money and say, "Thanks! Have a great day." After they left, you'd throw away their slip and put their money in your pocket, without ringing up the sale. There would be no record of the transaction at all. It wouldn't have worked if the dry cleaners was on a computer system, but it was an old neighborhood place, and they were still using a regular cash register.

"Lorinda is an asshole," one of the girls, Marie, told me. "I've been working here for over a year and she won't give me a raise. That's why I don't feel bad about stealing from her."

Lorinda was the owner. She had hired me, even though I was only a junior and didn't have any job experience except baby-sitting. When I told Marie that I thought Lorinda was nice, she said, "Don't be such a sucker. She's nice to everyone in the beginning."

Marie was in community college. She had blond curly hair, and was always bragging about how she'd gone out and gotten drunk, then driven herself home. I thought about telling her that I was in the SADD chapter at my high school, but I knew she would only make fun of me.

I liked the other girl, Heidi, better. She stole from the till, too, but somehow she seemed like a nicer person than Marie. Besides working at the dry cleaners, she also had a part-time job at the mall as an assistant window dresser. In the fall, she was going to move to New York City and start school at the Fashion Institute of Technology.

On weeknights, I worked with either Marie or Heidi. On Saturdays, we all worked together. Since I was the last one hired, I got stuck with most of the marking-in, while Marie and Heidi worked the front counter. That meant I had to tag all the dirty clothes that had been dropped off, then put them in the wooden bin that corresponded to the day the customer wanted to pick them up. I also had to check everyone's pockets. It felt weird, sticking my hands in people's clothes like that. Especially when I found something. Usually it was just a pen or a tie clip, but on my third Saturday, I pulled out a ten-dollar bill.

"Lucky!" Marie said. She had just come back to check on me. Then she yelled, "Hey, Heidi! Robin just found ten bucks!"

Heidi popped her head around the corner. "Cool," she said. "You can buy us some donuts."

"I'm going to give it back," I told the two of them.

They looked at me.

"How do I do that?" I asked.

Marie made a face. "Don't ask me," she said, and she went back out front.

Heidi was quiet for a second, then she said, "Put it in an envelope, then staple it to their ticket. When they come in, it'll be right there, in the file."

"Okay," I said. "Thanks."

"No problem," she said, and her head disappeared.

Later, Marie watched while I put the money in the envelope, then wrote the customer's name, Mr. Brill, on the outside. "Just so you know," she said, "that guy is an asshole."

I didn't answer her, just licked the envelope.

"He's this grumpy old man who never says please or thank you."

"It's still his money," I said.

Marie ignored me for the rest of the day. I tried to make friends with her by asking about her classes, but she only gave me boring answers. Then she turned around and acted all fun and happy with Heidi. At lunch time, she used some of the money she'd stolen from the exact change customers that morning to get food from Burger King. She bought me a hamburger, but I wouldn't eat it. "Jesus," she said. "Are you trying to make me feel bad or what?"

"No," I said. "I'm not."

"Freakin' good-goody," she muttered.

Heidi didn't defend me, but she didn't say anything mean, either. She just sat at the seamstress's table, popping fries in her mouth.

My dad picked me up at six o'clock, and asked how my day had gone. "Okay," I said.

"What's wrong?" he said.

"Nothing."

"I can't wait to get free dry cleaning," he said. "We're going to save a bundle."

He was talking about my new privileges. After my first month on the job, as long as everything was going okay,

Lorinda had told me that my family and I could start bringing our clothes in. Both my parents had been wearing dirty suits to work for the last week, in anticipation of the big day.

At the next SADD meeting, Mrs. Keoghan went over our upcoming activities, then asked if anyone had any issues they'd like to discuss. I raised my hand and said, "I work with this girl who's always bragging about driving drunk. I don't know what I should do about it."

Mrs. Keoghan asked if any of the other kids had suggestions for me, and people said things like invite her to come to one of our meetings, or tell her some statistics, or introduce her to one of the parents whose kids had died from drunk driving. I said those were all good ideas, even though I knew that I wouldn't use any of them. Later, I felt kind of badly. I think I hadn't really wanted to get advice about Marie. I think I'd just wanted to show off that I knew someone who got drunk.

On my fourth Saturday, I went to work with a big bag of my parents' clothes. I assumed I'd be doing the marking-in, but when I got there, Marie had taken my place in the back. She said she had a migraine and didn't feel like dealing with customers. "Are those your clothes?" she asked, nodding toward my bag.

"Yes."

"Well, give them to me," she said.

"That's okay," I said. "I can mark them in myself." I was embarrassed because they kind of smelled.

"Don't fight with me," Marie snapped, and she came over and took the bag out of my hands. "I'm not in the mood."

"But they're dirty," I said.

"Duh," she said, dumping the clothes out onto the counter.

I went out front to help Heidi then. "Marie's in a bad mood," she whispered.

I nodded.

Then Heidi made a motion like she was drinking from a bottle and we both laughed.

"What's so funny?" Marie called.

"Nothing," Heidi called back.

A second later, Marie came out waving a twenty dollar bill. "Look what I found," she said.

"Where'd you get that?" I asked.

"Your dad's pocket."

"Give it back," I said, reaching for it, but she pulled her hand away.

"Finders keepers," Marie said.

"Marie!" Heidi said. "Not if it's her dad's!"

"Why not?" Marie said.

Heidi looked at her like she was crazy. Then she grabbed her purse and went outside for a smoke.

Marie shrugged and put the money in her pocket.

"Give it back," I said again, but we both knew that wasn't going to happen.

That night, a few of us from SADD went out on a drive-along with the police. That was where you sat in the back of the cruiser and watched the cops pull people over at roadblocks. Only a few kids got to go every year. I won my spot by selling the most T-shirts for Ghost Day, which was when you walked around with white makeup on and remembered people who had died from bad decisions.

I'd never really seen a drunk person before, but then the cops started pulling them over, one by one. They had to try to walk in a straight line, or else touch their fingers to their noses. If they failed, the police put handcuffs on them and drove down to the station.

It was strange, but I kept wishing that one of the drunk people would be Marie. Every time the cops asked someone to step outside their car, I waited for the sight of her bouncy blond curls, shining in the moonlight. I wanted her to get in trouble for something. I wanted her to get caught. Not for her own good, but for mine. So I could stop feeling like it was so bad to be a goody-goody.

On Monday, Marie and I worked alone together. I did the marking-in, and she worked the counter. I liked listening to the sound of the bell ringing every time a customer came in. I liked listening to Marie ask people what their phone numbers were and when they wanted to pick up their dry cleaning. It was a whole other side of her. A polite side.

After I finished the marking-in, I went out front to help. I was careful to let Marie wait on all the cute men, while I took all the older people and tired-looking women. When there was a lull in business, Marie said, "Guess what I did with your dad's money?"

"What?" I said.

"I got wasted," she said.

"Oh."

"Then I was driving home," she said, "and some cop pulled me over."

I looked at her. I couldn't believe it.

"Want to know what he said?" she asked me.

"Sure," I said, trying to sound cool.

"He said, 'You've got a busted tail light. I'll let you off with a warning, but you need to get it fixed.'"

I didn't know what to say to that.

"I'll never, ever get caught," Marie said. "Ever."

"It's not just that," I said. "You could get killed."

"Nope," she said. "I'll never get killed, either."

"Do you want to know the statistics?" I asked her.

"Nope," she said again.

"Well," I said, "there are 2.6 million drunk driving crashes each year."

"I told you I didn't want to hear it!" she said. "Are you deaf?"

"No."

"You don't know anything about anything," she said.

"I'm in SADD," I told her.

"What?" she said.

"Students Against Drunk Driving."

"God!" she said. "You think you're so much better than me!"

"No, I don't," I said.

"I can't stand it," she said. "I wish it was just me and Heidi again."

We didn't talk for the rest of the night. A couple of people paid in exact change, and Marie cheered up a little to have the extra money. Then, before we closed, an old man came in. I stepped up to wait on him, but Marie said, "That's okay, I got it." It turned out he was the guy who'd left the ten dollars in his pocket. The one who never said please or thank you. "Mr. Brill?" Marie said to him now, handing over the envelope. "We found this money in your pants pocket."

"Oh," he said. "Thank you." He opened the envelope and pulled out the bill. "Well, I'll be damned," he said. Then he looked at Marie and said, "You're a good girl."

I wanted to tell him that it wasn't true. That she wasn't good at all. That she was mean, and she drove drunk, and she stole. But then she smiled at him a little, like she took it as a compliment, and I decided not to say anything.

THE 52-HERTZ WHALE

JORDAN WIKLUND

The 52-Hz whale is alone. Whales travel in family units called pods, and the combined total of whales identified with the voice of the 52-Hz whale number this many: one.

-

March, 1857: the earth passes perfectly between the sun and the moon, hiding the moon completely in its shadow. This event is known as a total lunar eclipse. Heinrich Rudolph Hertz is born a month earlier in Hamburg, Germany.

-

The 52-Hz whale was first recorded by a nuclear submarine in 1988, and has been tracked by underwater hydrophone recordings ever since, suspended in the deep. Nothing else sounds like the 52-Hz whale, so its journeys are easy to document: it swims beneath the swooping arm of Alaska's Aleutian isles and north and south along the Pacific coast of America. Its migration path is unlike that of any known whale. In 20 years of monitoring the 52-Hz whale, its pitch has deepened somewhat—matured—to 51 Hz, 50 Hz, maybe even 49 Hz, but still, we call it what we first knew it by.

-

Hertz is credited with discovering the existence of electromagnetic waves. Invisible and intangible, electromagnetic waves are often measured by their frequency—the number of repeated events (waves) per unit time—and a *Hertz* is a measure of frequency by cycles per second. Thus, a second hand on a grandfather clock may be said to operate at 1 Hertz (Hz), or one cycle per second, with each orbital tick around the clock's face.

Sound is conducted by electromagnetic waves, and *pitch* is how we perceive of and distinguish between high and low sounds. High sounds have high frequencies and low sounds have low frequencies.

-

The moon orbits the earth at roughly 380.5 nanohertz (nHz), or, properly notated, $3.805*10^{-7}$ cycles per second.

-

Whalesong is an accepted nomenclature of the species' communication. Whales often call in 20-30 minute bursts, but sometimes the calls can last for days, and whales of the same family sing slightly altered versions of the same whalesong.

Water does not pool on the lunar surface. It decomposes in a process called photodissociation, succumbing to the molecular assault of photons carried by Hertz' electromagnetic waves from the sun. Nothing to swim through; in nothing to sink.

-

Most whales communicate in a range from 15 to 25 Hz, so the plight of the 52-Hz whale is twofold.

Some whales can't hear the 52-Hz whale.

Those who can don't know what it is.

-

In his youth, young Heinrich showed a remarkable aptitude for language. He learned the hard consonants and sickle-shaped letters of Arabic, an alphabet riddled with fins. He even wrote letters to his family in Sanskrit, parsing the singular vowels from the layered diphthongs, the orbital anusvara from the exclamatory visarga. He knew the staccato'd plosives and fricatives, the airy nasals.

-

The voice of the 52-Hz whale—stuttering clicks, warbling trills, and long, sonorous bellows—identify it as a member of the family *Mysticeti,* baleen whales like the giant blue and the hobbled humpback. These whales loom through the water, mouths agape, filtering microorganisms through comb-like plates of keratin called baleen. With their mouths open, they often appear to be smiling, as if laughing at a joke.

-

When the moon is full, what do you see? In the darker patches visible to the naked eye, some see a warty, hobbled crone, or a grinning skull. Some Inuit cultures of Alaska see a man in the moon—a man who safeguards the souls of animals after they die.

-

October, 1879: outside the school, a young man looks at the moon. He is 21 years old. The Munich air slips under Heinrich's topcoat, pebbles his arms. He has always loved meteorology, but it is hard for him to imagine how vast the universe might be; it chills him more than the wind. Professor von Bezold studies dust, air, the scorched earth of a lightning strike. Heinrich has just returned from his mentor's office.

He isn't as interested in dust, or the crackling, angry skies. He looks at the moon and thinks: waning gibbous. He looks at the moon and thinks: he wants to know more. He wants to know what is behind the lightning, beneath it, what moves before and after it. He wants to know: what is left once the vision of the thing is gone?

-

Relentless, relentless, relentless in its youth, searching. From 1993-1994, the 52-Hz whale swam over 1,800 miles below Alaska, east to west and back again. The next year, it swam over 1,200 miles north to south, up and down the coasts of California, Oregon, and Washington. The years add up. The 52-Hz whale keeps searching.

-

Look at the moon, and see what you see—see the dark patches of the lunar surface. Hear their names: *Mare Frigoris*, Sea of Cold. *Mare Imbrium*, Sea of Showers and Rain. *Oceanus Procellarum*, Ocean of Storms. *Mare Serenitatis*, Sea of Serenity. *Mare Tranquillitatis*, Sea of Tranquility. *Mare Crisium*, Sea of Crisis. *Mare Fecunditatis*, Sea of Fecundity. *Mare Nectaris*, Sea of Nectar. *Mare Vaporum*, Sea of Vapors. *Mare Insularum*, Sea of Islands. *Mare Nubium*, Sea of Clouds. *Mare Humorum*, Sea of Moisture. *Mare Cognitum*, Sea That Has Become Known.

Upset by her lack of water, the moon exerts her influence on the Earth, prompting high tide, low tide, an interstellar conversation.

-

Red sky at night, sailors delight! It's true, to a point: red sunsets occur when high concentrations of dust particles are illumined by the sun, glinting in a high-pressure atmosphere. Red skies usually indicate impending tidal stability.

-

Beholden to the waning and waxing cycles of the moon, the frequency of the ocean's waves whispering against the earth's shores at any given moment is incalculable.

-

Hertz theorized that light is itself a wave, and travels both within and beyond itself. The legacy of Hertz's studies cannot be overstated—his experiments helped define reflection, refraction, polarization, interference, and the velocity of waves.

-

Breaching is the curious habit of whales leaping out of the water and into the air. Scientists loosely differentiate *breaching* from *lunging*, because of one simple fact: breaching whales intend for their entire bodies to clear the surface of the water.

-

Fever in morning, divers take warning! Decompression sickness occurs when a sudden loss of internal pressure causes the body's vessels to swell, such as when divers ascend to the surface too quickly. Decompression sickness often presents as fever, deep joint and muscle ache, temporary paralysis, and painful vasculitis, or inflammation of the blood vessels. In rare cases, this swelling of organs can be fatal.

-

Find a tuba. Blow into it, hard. Have an experienced tuba player ("tubist") show you the lowest possible note, then adjust accordingly for the note just above it. Again, with gusto. This is what 52 Hz sounds like.

-

Naturally, one should be able to communicate underwater; the speed of sound is four times greater. Low-frequency baleen whales create the loudest sounds on Earth. Before motorized boats, the ocean was quieter. Before motorized boats, it is speculated that whales could communicate from pole to pole, cacophonous.

-

"It's of no use whatsoever," Hertz said, before his discoveries were made. "We just have these mysterious electromagnetic waves that we cannot see with the naked eye."

-

If a whale calls in the ocean, and no whales are there to hear it, can the whale be said to have called at all?

-

"But they are there," Hertz added.

-

Skilled tubists are able to create privileged tones, also called *false tones,* which test the limits of human auditory capabilities, such as in William Kraft's "Encounters II" for tuba. Listen: hear the double-pedal C. Listen: at two minutes, seventeen seconds, just so: a series of staccato blurts, footsteps in the next room, maybe echoes of footsteps.

-

In Tarot, the moon is the card of illusion and falsities, of monthly cycles, imagination and subconscious. Its astrological number is 18, a numerical harbinger of change (1+8 = 9, the number of endings before a new cycle begins at 1).

Asked about the ramifications of his discoveries, Hertz replied, "*Nothing, I guess.*"

One fact scientists have discerned: baleen whales, like dolphins and orcas, use echolocation to find one another. To see though through the depths.

Stop me if you've heard this one: a whale goes to the doctor. "I'm Henry," the doctor says, "what's your name?" The whale's voice shakes the room as it tells the doctor its name. "I can't understand you," the doctor says. The whale swings its head from side to side and flaps its fins up and down. It dents the exam table with its tail. It knocks over a lamp, a jar of tongue suppressors, and the doctor. The doctor, accustomed to difficult patients, adjusts his glasses and sits up on one elbow, looking up at the whale. "Show me where it Hertz," he says. The whale's tears drown them both.

When Hertz thought of his work, did it look like this?

W_avesseva_wW_avesseva_wW_avesseva_wW

a_{vesse}va_wW_avesseva_wW_avesseva_wW

a_{vesse}va_wW_avesseva_{ww}W_avesseva_wW_ave

sse_va_{ww}W_avesseva_wW_avesseva_{ww}W_aves

"his experiments helped define reflection / \ reflection define helped experiments his"

Fact: no evidence exists that baleen whales call for emotive purposes.

Fact: for us to hear them at all, whalesong is sped up 10-20 times to bring the ultra-low-frequency waves into our auditory range.

Conclusion: what we perceive as whalesong is false, a cacophony of false tones.

-

When is a whale not a whale?

When it's *a-wailing*.

-

The light of the moon isn't true light at all; it's a reflection, never the same from night to night. In the light of the moon, everything seems to change.

But if everything appears differently, how can this light be false?

-

Relentless, relentless, Hertz "helped define reflection, refraction,

polarization

-

Inter—

-

—FERENCE—

-

andthe*velocity*ofwaves."

-

—numbers this many: one—

—total eclipse—

—the 52-Hz whale—

—"it's of no use," he said—

—the lunar surface—

—can't understand—

—when is a whale—

—take warning—

-

Hertz died in 1894, at 36 years of age. It was January 1, the start of the new year at the end of the 19th century. He succumbed to Wegener's granulomatosis, an incurable form of vasculitis. He has no living descendants. Whatever secrets he harbored died with him.

-

"Syzygy."

"Use it in a sentence?"

"A syzygy occurs when three celestial bodies in the same gravitational system are aligned."

"Syzygy. S-Y-Z-Y-G-Y. Syzygy."

-

If he had lived a while longer, Hertz might have gazed out his bedroom window. He might have witnessed another lunar eclipse on September 29. He might have remembered his youth, the Munich breeze on an autumn day. He might have seen the moon, wondrous of such a thing.

-

The light of the moon strikes the surface of the water, distorting, bending every object beneath. Are they false? Are they real?

-

To return to one's self: the gift of an echo carried by a wave, suspended between the resonating past, the infrequent future. Reflect, refract; see yourself anew. Ascend, ascend, breach, and align—it is more beautiful than you ever imagined. Seas of Serenity and Tranquility, Sea of Being Known. A release of internal pressure—a swelling of the heart, it is too much, too much. Syzyged between above and below, the pressures within and without. Not a death, but an embrace.

SUSU AT THE STATE FAIR

ALIA HAMADA

There is nothing like a bacon wrapped hot dog.
There is nothing like a free Beach Boys concert to an Arab in moonlight.
        It feels so intimate, so simple, like baby's breath
in a fancy bouquet.
Susu in a Phoenix Suns sweatshirt, hands, clapping above his head.

Wouldn't it be nice?

Susu knew he won.
But, only sometimes.

Susu, cramped from crying, he rarely ate.
Susu slept in the basement of a restaurant, played solitaire, smoked Marlboros.

        Zero of this had any meaning for his family back home.

A camel glares at Susu at the fair.
$3.00 for a photo, climb on top with a stepstool.

        The camel glares, and glares.

Susu buys Indian Fry Bread, as someone else pays $3.00
for a photo with the camel.

There is nothing like losing at balloon toss.
As he tossed and tossed, Susu reached for the sky, in search of a different

kind of night. The kind he thought would be happening,
happening right now.

Did Susu remove his hat? This is all the camel sees.
He keeps up his stare.

And, then Susu runs, and runs,
leaving crumbs for someone to follow.

SUSU ESCAPES CAIRO, ONCE

ALIA HAMADA

Pretty boy in a sailboat shirt
leans,
   against, a cart of cracked melon,
   sweet,

filled, with flies,
at the rind,
   gnaw the crone glass. Heat,
   isolation, belong here

in upper lip dander.
Eye of heaven simpers
   at pink flesh, syrup on the marl.
   Sugar clogs the alley's

underbelly. Men,
three shirt buttons,
   unbuttoned.
   Women, in the window,
elbows out.

Dust,
   rush, in the wafting,
   the onion smell in buses,
babies,
stumble into cars.

   This is not a drill.
   Honeyed, street signs,
eyes peek behind black cotton.

Susu drags,
   sticks across vapors.
   When the end, hits,
don't act surprised.

A bloom of sea sand,
   coats, the innards
   of his pith, marrow.

SUSU IN THE FOREST

ALIA HAMADA

People here believe in a different Africa.
Here, there is just one box to check.
Susu checks Other and calls it an afternoon.

He arrived and immediately: swarmed
by tree dander and wasps, moist pollen.
Susu wrestles ants for a bed

under rocks. Every stone smells of apricot,
dank and fruity. From olive to beige
to a possum's underside,

Susu's skin bleaches from shade.
His nose, made of crackled timber,
bends out of shape when nudged.

Cramped breath, a muddled wheeze
lurches from his middle to forehead.
The way he walks now, stumbling

in mud. Everything is sopping.
Misplacement, they say in el Zeitoun
where fava beans boil in ghee.

They remember his eyes, oily.
They remember his teeth, crooked.
Staring out into morning dust,

on concrete balconies, they believe
Susu is dead, trampled over,
and under, a speeding spill of milk.

Susu exhales postage stamps. Possums
die. People pray Susu! Susu! like a
football chant, like the Olympics.

A raccoon on his head, we call Susu
David. He smells like popcorn, American
movies where the screen whitens,

and everything is starry.

BEFORE YOU GO

MICHELLE DEAN

Ben hated the sound of newer phones—"Birdsong my ass," he'd told a particularly eager salesperson at Radio Shack, though not unkindly—so the only ringer on in the house was on the kitchen phone, a canary-yellow rotary model from another lifetime. The bell on that one was cold and clean and could cut through the whole house, and during the day they were on the main floor anyway.

Though she'd been waiting as long as he had, out there on the summer porch, Gretchen let Ben answer. She decided not to meet his eyes when he glanced at her before disappearing inside. She did, however, listen for his customary slow groan of a "Hell—Oh," which came along as promised. These days, Ben always sounded upset to hear from anyone other than the girls.

Gretchen was crocheting an afghan in purples and blues—colors of valor, she thought. Gretchen did not have an eye for the things that went together, which exasperated her daughters when they were young and had to wear whatever she'd bought for them. Christy, in particular, had hated her mother's habit of pairing turquoise and orange and spent most of her adult life trying to convince Gretchen to look at things a little differently. When Christie dropped by the day before, she had told Gretchen the afghan was "very technicolor dreamcoat" in a tone that suggested no sane person could ever want such a garment.

Sometimes, Gretchen hated the way her daughter talked, but she had said nothing, because arguments with Christy were not worth the effort. The child was a sweet-talker from birth, charming adults with a vocabulary that included "impenetrable" by age four. At first, to Ben and Gretchen, this was a pretty parlor trick for the neighbours. But Christy came to use words like cattleprods. It was never possible to speak to her before breakfast, possibly because Christy was invariably outpacing you by three cups or more.

"Mmm, I see," came Ben's voice from the kitchen. "Well, when do you want me to come in?"

Gretchen kept making loops and knots and pulling them through. The afghan was to be in a chevron pattern, too old-fashioned for 2006. Gretchen was not making it for anyone in particular, of course. Probably it would end up in the guest room closet with some of her other projects—the empty scrapbook and attendant supplies, the macramé plant holders and the children's book about a household of fairies, half-written and a quarter-illustrated.

"Thanks, Jeff. I'll see you then."

Ben ambled into the living room, shuffling his slippers along the carpet. The soles of the slippers were falling off, and flopped if he took proper, foot-off-the-ground steps. But never you mind, he told Christy when she grabbed his arm one day. This was his new way of walking. He had been a man of purposeful strides not so very long ago, before the diagnosis and the needles and the hours in reclining chairs. Before waiting by the toilet for the next wave of heaving up what seemed like buckets of everything he had ever eaten, let alone that day's meal, which he barely ate. He'd always been skinny, though, and lucky that was so because even people who knew him didn't know about the sickness, unless he told them himself. Or Gretchen did. He had been in remission, but the doctor had just run some new tests after Ben kept falling down a lot. Sometimes he was on the floor when Gretchen came home, reading a book, claiming he liked it there. She tried not to let herself think of him crawling.

"We should get you new ones," Gretchen said, eyes still on the crochet hook.

"Eh?" Ben settled into his chair, a worn leather barcalounger he'd had since before they'd been married.

"New slippers."

"I s'pose. I like these, though, got them broken in."

Gretchen smiled at him, not widely, but she was looking at him straight on, the way she knew he liked her to, so he could tell whether it was real. Her eyes were brown, and much more striking, she thought, now that her hair was gray.

"Can't beat the real thing," Ben said, which is what he always said when he thought the smile was genuine. Then, after a moment: "Jeff says, it's going to be harder going this time."

Gretchen looked back at her afghan.

"I'm going to have to go to Ottawa for a bit."

Loop, hook, pull and stitch.

"Probably six weeks, Jeff said. I guess I'll stay with Mary again."

She said nothing.

"Six weeks is a long time," he said, looking at her.

Gretchen lifted her gaze, looking out the screen window of the porch at nothing in particular. "That's a lovely house they have, there."

"Yup," he said, but there was a question in it, and not one she cared to answer. She went to stir the stew she had made in the crock-pot that morning.

When, thirty-five years before, Gretchen's sister Margaret had gotten married, she had insisted on a stag-and-doe party. It was uncomfortable. It was not that having the party itself was unusual: in those days you spent the summers after high school drifting from one party to the next. It was that Margaret herself had had two other stag-

and-doe parties, but both times had shied at some point before the actual wedding. The guests at this third attempt were therefore more hesitant in their revelry than they might otherwise have been. (This was perhaps also due to the less generous apportionment of alcohol—Margaret and Gretchen's father had cut the budget short.) Still, the hall was festooned in purple and white steamers—Margaret's favorites, and the local high school's colors to boot. Every table had a centerpiece of pansies, which tiny cousins had been sent into the fields to find earlier that day, so as to tired them out for the older ones who would babysit them.

Sitting alone at the family table, Gretchen, whose hair was then long and red—she only cut it short after Christy was born, after looking young stopped mattering to her—was quietly sweating her way through a cotton shirt dress. It was August, and she was heavily pregnant with another of her daughters, Jenny, then. This pregnancy had been difficult, and personally, Gretchen blamed Robert for that.

Robert, whom Gretchen had married right out of the gate at eighteen, was gone off with a girl from the convenience store. To make his fortune in the States, he said. The girl wanted to be an actress, and he had some idea of being a writer, "like Louis L'Amour," he said. Gretchen was the picture of practicality, the gossips said. She didn't yell or scream, or even ask to be taken along. It was out of the question. Two months after he was gone, when she had to face facts, she ignored the girlfriends, and even her own mother, who spoke of "things you can do." Now, she just winced whenever she thought of how the baby had come to be, and tried to put it out of her mind. But bitterness was creeping up on her, especially as her body became harder and harder to manage.

In her current condition, there was no question of dancing, so Gretchen just sat and watched as others did. The air conditioning was out, so there were only ceiling fans to cool the place, and everyone's faces glistened. For awhile, her eyes skipped through the crowd on the linoleum dance floor, lingering on the younger couples, noting odd combinations—Jess Marquette and Paul Wallace, for example, who were supposed to dislike each other on account of Paul's brother jilting Jess's sister years back. But eventually the thrill of gathering new gossip receded, and Gretchen closed her eyes, fanning herself with a napkin. Pretty soon after her eyes closed, Gretchen, who was starting to feel a bit feverish, began to sense someone else's eyes on her.

This is the point at which Gretchen and Ben, telling this story years later, would begin to trip over each other. Gretchen always maintained that Ben borrowed his version of events from one of his beloved old movies, undoubtedly one starring Barbara Stanwyck, a crush of his. Ben would chuckle, and say that Gretchen just didn't want to admit that she had ever lost control.

Ben did have the upper hand, because he was conscious to see the red-haired girl he'd been admiring—he had had a weakness for redheads, his ex-wife was one too—stand straight up in the hall. He looked away for a second, embarrassed that she might have noticed him watching her, and also because now he saw she was pregnant, and thus certainly married. When he looked back, he saw that she was pointing at him, and the blood rushed to his face. Gretchen tried to say something, and then, she fell.

At this point Gretchen liked to take over the telling again, and would say that she awoke to the rather tanned face of a skinny man with inky black hair staring down at her. He handed her a glass of water. She drank it, looking at him over the rim of the glass, like a child. He smiled at her, and she, rather than looking away coquettishly like the other women he had known, smiled back, looking him straight in the eye. (Ben sometimes liked to interject here that he had noticed her lack of a wedding band while she'd been out.) Without thinking, he said, "Next time you've got something to say, just say it, alright?"

It was the first time in Gretchen's whole life that anyone had really cared what she had to say.

"And that," Ben would add, proudly, "was the moment Gretchen chose me."

In truth, the process was a little longer than that. Gretchen found herself shocked when, six months later, Ben proposed. She was sitting on the old plaid chesterfield in the little house she had rented with Robert. Ben was beside her, and beside them, in the third seat, was his daughter Mary holding the sleeping four-month-old Jenny. She sputtered, and he dropped the subject. It took Gretchen another six months to say yes. Everyone said, how lucky that they found each other, two single parents. In fact, even then, the moment Gretchen chose Ben, in her own head, was almost a year later, when Christy was born. The fainting was just the opening of the door. Christy pulled Gretchen right through and slammed it shut. But Gretchen never interrupted to clarify whenever they got telling the story.

About a month after the phone call, it was almost time to go. They had not talked about it, much, other than to exchange pertinent information. The date he had to be there, whether he would take the car or a bus. (Bus, it was decided, without discussing that it was, after all, their only car.) What kind of hospital stay he was looking at, how long it might be before he could travel. The length and girth of the needles, which he'd looked up on the internet. The grace period, after the first treatment, before the "crap," as Ben put it, would set in. The possibility of her crocheting him a skullcap or two. Gretchen always punctuated these exchanges with a gesture of affection. She'd ruffle his remaining hair, knead a bony shoulder, ask him if he wanted a square from the freezer.

They were not talkers and never had been. It was, in her view, why they got along so well. Gretchen watched enough television to know that in other places, in other worlds, women were not like her. They talked to each other about things and got the impulse out that way, kept it from torturing their husbands. For her own part she'd just never had much to say, and so was grateful instead to live in a place where marriages had balustrades and scaffolding hiding the interior. You talked to others at the supermarket to exchange recipes and yarn brands. You had them over for dinner and talked of the news, taxes, the maintenance you did on the house. Nothing else.

One afternoon, Gretchen was folding shirts in the bedroom. Ben was in the study next door, reading a detective novel he'd bought the day before. He was almost finished already. He had a rule—one detective novel, then one classic—but he always seemed to get through the potboilers faster.

"Before you go," she called, "can you please call the man about the gutters?"

"Mmm," said Ben, in a way Gretchen knew meant he wasn't listening.

Gretchen stuck her head in the study door, holding one of Ben's shirts with her chin while she folded in the sleeves.

"Please, Ben, they're just better at listening to men."

Ben glanced at her momentarily. "Sure, fine."

"Thank you." She went back to the bedroom.

"You'll be lonely without me, you know," he said, tentatively. Then, louder: "What'll you do?"

It took her a minute. "Oh, you know, the church stuff, and the bazaar is soon, and the young people never help with that, anymore."

Gretchen finished the shirts, and the pants, and balled his socks. After admiring its orderliness, she zipped up the clothes suitcase with purpose.

"Now, then, what books are you taking?" She strode into the study with his bookbag, left over from the days he had worked as a middle school teacher. She began scanning the bookcase, ready to pack them for him.

 He was silent, so she turned to look at him. He was no longer reading, just looking out the window at the white ash he'd planted twenty years ago, when they bought the house.

"Ben?"

"*Crime and Punishment*," he said, after a moment.

"Okay."

"*For Whom The Bell Tolls.*"

"Mmmhmm."

"*A Good Man Is Hard To Find.*"

There was a slight failing in his voice. She looked at him, but he went on without meeting her eyes, speaking quickly, "*The Stranger. Family Matters. Beloved—*"

"Ben." She sat down on a chair, and looked at him, still holding the books, the bookbag over her shoulder.

He still refused to look at her. She suppressed the impulse to ask what was wrong. What a silly question. The man had cancer, he was her husband. How tired she had become of being asked it herself. Even her own daughters asked, sometimes. When Christy did, just the week before, Gretchen had known what she'd been asking.

"I'm fine," she said, trying to avoid this, glancing around the restaurant as she sipped her tea after lunch.

"Are you?"

"Yes, for chrissakes stop asking." Gretchen had become a prodigious user of curse words in her old age. "Your Dad and I knew this was coming, knew there would be more of the chemo and the in-patient stuff."

"I just wanted to ask without Dad around." Christy spoke the words with deliberate caution, annoying her mother.

"Why? The answer wouldn't be any different."

"Well," Christy tried, this time consciously diplomatic, "should you be, you know, fine?"

"Please, Christy, not today."

"It's just, you have been married to the man over thirty years, and he's really really really sick, and he's got to go, and you're staying, and Jenny, Mary and I just don't—"

"Enough. Do you hear me? Enough."

Christy was silent. The conversation stopped there, right on the edge. Christy was blunt and argumentative, but no one would ever say she was a fool. Gretchen was proud of that.

Ben was not as direct as Christy, but he wanted to know the same thing. He just didn't want to have to ask.

After a few moments of silence, anxious ones on her part, Gretchen no longer thought Ben was ignoring her. He was just somewhere else. She sat there with him for what seemed like an hour but was probably less than ten minutes. Idly, she wondered what had transfixed him. He kept on looking out the window. Maybe it was the ash, its leaves a deep, deep green fed by all the rain they'd been having, and swaying in an otherworldly breeze that neither of them could feel in the room. Maybe it was the sky through it, appearing mostly as light mottled with blue in between swaying branches. Maybe he was not seeing anything at all. At first, Gretchen thought she shouldn't interrupt. But she couldn't stop herself.

"Mary will be here in an hour."

Ben blinked, twice, and his eyes turned to her. Gretchen suddenly knew that her last guess had been the best one. He hadn't been looking at anything at all. He was beginning to see the wall, to see the way things had to go, and sometimes he just had to look real hard to believe it. Gretchen knew the feeling.

"I know," he finally said, his voice a little raspy.

She smiled at him, eyes wide open, eager like a child wanting to please, and waited for the inevitable response that just this once, in the whole time they knew each other, never came.

SAUCER OF MILK

ELENA DUFF

EMPTY NEST

ELENA DUFF

LIFE IS SWEET

ELENA DUFF

ICE PLATE

ELENA DUFF

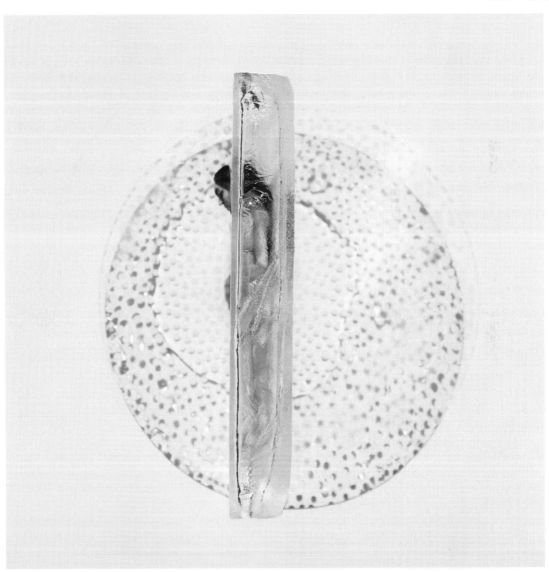

CONTRIBUTORS

Cristin O'Keefe Aptowicz was recently awarded a 2011 National Endowment for the Arts Fellowship in Poetry. Her work has been published in *Conduit, Rattle, Barrelhouse, La Petite Zine,* and *McSweeney's Internet Tendencies,* among others. She is the author of five books of poetry, most recently *Everything is Everything* (Write Bloody Publishing), and the nonfiction poetry slam history, *Words in Your Face* (Soft Skull Press). As the 2010-2011 ArtsEdge Writer-in-Residence at the University of Pennsylvania, she spent the year researching her next nonfiction book on the founder of Philadelphia's (in)famous, medical oddity-filled Mutter Museum. For more information, please visit www.aptowicz.com.

Matthew Baker was born in Fort Wayne, Indiana. His Internet novella *Kaleidoscope* can be read at www.kaleidoscopeof.com.

Rusty Barnes lives in Revere MA but grew up in Mosherville, PA, population 300 or less. He is the sole proprietor of the blogazine *Fried Chicken and Coffee* (www.friedchickenandcoffee.com).

Jeremy Bauer is currently pursuing an MFA in another dimension with his wife and robot. His work has been featured in such magazines as *Red Lightbulbs, Everyday Genius,* and *Spooky Boyfriend.* His chapbook, *The Jackalope Wars,* was released by Stoked Press in 2010. He blogs at OhBabyOhMan.blogspot.com. His gift is your antennae.

Nathan Blake's writing has appeared or is forthcoming in *Monkeybicycle, Word Riot, Bluestem,* and *Tulane Review,* among others. He is currently a part-time janitor in Virginia's non-profit sector and a proud member of the 3-4-5 writing community.

Sommer Browning writes poems, draws comics and tells jokes. She is the author of *Either Way I'm Celebrating* (Birds, LLC, 2011), a collection of poems and comics. She also has three chapbooks out, most recently *THE BOWLING* (Greying Ghost, 2010) with Brandon Shimoda. With Julia Cohen she curates The Bad Shadow Affair, a reading series in Denver. Follow her on Twitter [https://twitter.com/#!/VagTalk].

Elizabeth Cantwell is currently a PhD student in the Literature & Creative Writing Program at the University of Southern California. She relies on her stupidly adorable corgi mix and her fellow writer/roommate/husband to survive in Los Angeles. Her work has recently appeared in such journals as *Indiana Review, La Petite Zine, RHINO, The Cortland Review,* and *The Los Angeles Review.*

Sérah Carter is a carbon-based life form residing in Maryland whose existence generally includes ringing up customers at a corporate bookstore, writing, rejection, the occasional acceptance, and collecting dead things to hang on walls. This is her first grown-up publication.

Rebecca Cook writes poetry and prose and has published in journals such as *New England Review, New Orleans Review,* and *Northwest Review*. Her chapbook of poems, *The Terrible Baby,* is available from Dancing Girl Press. Her first novel, *Click,* is forthcoming from Kitsune Books in 2013.

Brandon Courtney was born and raised in Adel, Iowa. He served four years in the United States Navy. His poetry and flash fiction is forthcoming or appears in *Best New Poets 2009, Linebreak, BOXCAR Poetry Review, The Journal, The Raleigh Review, Smokelong Quarterly, Tar River Review, Gargoyle* and *The Los Angeles Review* among many others, and has twice been nominated for a Pushcart Prize. He was also recently nominated for the *Best of the Net Anthology,* and is a finalist for the Oboh Poetry Prize. He attends the MFA program at Hollins University.

Michelle Dean is a writer, journalist and lawyer who lives, for the moment, in Queens. This is her first published piece of fiction.

Elena Duff is an Irish artist who was born in London and now lives and works in Berlin, Germany. Her work covers a broad range of media from painting to sculpture and photography. She's currently concentrating on her latest series of works, which consist of small figures sculpted from polymer clay. For more information and images visit www.elenaduff.com. The artwork for the cover was created by Elena.

Alicia Erian is the author of a story collection, *The Brutal Language of Love,* and a novel, *Towelhead,* which was made into a film by Alan Ball in 2008. Her forthcoming memoir, *The Dragon Lies Down,* will be published by Crown in the Spring of 2013.

Rebecca Morgan Frank is the author of *Little Murders Everywhere,* and her poems have appeared in such places as *Guernica, Post Road, Ploughshares, Copper Nickel,* and *Best New Poets 2008*. She is the recipient of the Poetry Society of America's 2010 Alice Fay di Castagnola Award. She is co-founder and editor of the online magazine *Memorious*.

Alia Hamada was born in Phoenix, AZ and received her MFA in Creative Writing from Lesley University's low-residency program. She currently lives in Somerville, MA and works at 826 Boston, a creative writing and tutoring center serving youth ages 6-18. Recent poetry has appeared in *Gigantic Sequins* and *elimae*.

Kathleen Hellen is a poet and the author of *The Girl Who Loved Mothra* (Finishing Line Press, 2010). Awards include the 2012 Washington Writers' Publishing House Prize in poetry, with her collection *Umberto's Night* forthcoming. Her poems have appeared recently in *Cimarron Review, The Evansville Review, Harpur Palate, Poemeleon,* and *Poetry Northwest* among others; and were featured on WYPR's The Signal.

Caitlin Horrocks is author of the story collection *This Is Not Your City*. Her work appears in *The New Yorker, The Best American Short Stories 2011, The PEN/O. Henry Prize Stories 2009, The Pushcart Prize XXXV,* and elsewhere. She lives in Grand Rapids, Michigan.

Kathryn Houghton holds an MFA from Eastern Washington University. She currently teaches at Michigan State University, writes book reviews for *The Collagist*, and blogs weekly at the *Willow Springs* blog, Bark.

Simon Jacobs is a young writer from Ohio. He edits the *Safety Pin Review* (safetypinreview.com), a new, wearable medium for fiction under 30 words. He leaves veiled confessions & love letters at simonajacobs.blogspot.com.

Hilary Jacqmin earned her BA in English from Wesleyan University and her MA in Writing Seminars from The Johns Hopkins University. She completed her MFA degree in poetry at the University of Florida this spring. Her poetry has appeared in *Best New Poets 2011, AGNI Online, Measure, The Urbanite, The Sewanee Theological Review,* and *Iron Horse Literary Review*. Her poem "World's Fair" won 3rd Prize in the 2010 *Atlantic* Student Writing Contest. Her poem "The Good Girl," published in *Controlled Burn*, was a winner of the 2010 AWP Intro Journals contest.

Eugenia Leigh is a Korean-American poet and Kundiman fellow who holds an MFA in Poetry from Sarah Lawrence College. She received the *Poets & Writers Magazine's* 2010 Amy Award, and her first poetry manuscript was a finalist for the 2011 National Poetry Series. Eugenia's poems have appeared in *North American Review, The Collagist, Lantern Review* and *Best New Poets 2010*, among other publications. Born in Chicago and raised in Los Angeles, she currently lives in Brooklyn.

D.W. Lichtenberg is the author of *THE ANCIENT BOOK OF HIP* (Fourteen Hills Press, 2009). He lives in San Francisco where he edits commercial video by day and *La Petite Zine* by night. He hopes to one day write the Great American Bumper Sticker. Learn more about his newest work, including his novel-in-progress, at DWLichtenberg.com.

Michael Martone was born in Fort Wayne, Indiana. He has taught at several universities including Johns Hopkins, Iowa State, Harvard, Alabama, and Syracuse. He participated in the last major memo war fought with actual paper memoranda before the advent of electronic email. Staples were deployed. The paper generated in that war stacks several inches deep, thick enough to stop a bullet. Martone learned that the "cc:" is the most strategic field of the memo's template, and he is sad to realize that fewer and fewer readers know what the "cc:" stands for let alone have ever held a piece of the delicate and duplicating artifact in their ink stained and smudge smudged fingers. It, like everything else, is history.

James May served as editor-in-chief of *New South* from 2008 until 2011. His poetry has recently appeared in *Green Mountains Review, New England Review, The New Republic,* and *Pleiades*. He lives in Decatur, Georgia, with his wife, the poet Chelsea Rathburn, and their newborn daughter.

Mark Neely's first book*, Beasts of the Hill*, won the *FIELD* Poetry Prize and will be published by Oberlin College Press in 2012. His chapbook, *Four of a Kind*, won the Concrete Wolf chapbook contest and came out in 2010. He directs the Creative Writing Program at Ball State University and is the editor of *The Broken Plate*.

Catherine Owen is a Vancouver poet and writer. She has published nine collections of poetry and one of prose. Her work has won the AB award and the Earle Birney prize and been nominated for many others, appeared in journals across North America and Europe, and been translated into three languages. You can find her at www.catherineowen.org.

Terrance Owens works as an editor in Seoul, South Korea. He got his MFA at Eastern Washington University.

Scott Pinkmountain (aka Scott Rosenberg) is a musician and a writer living in Joshua Tree, California. He's had recent work published in *The Rumpus* and *A Public Space*. He's released more than twenty albums and has recorded and performed with Anthony Braxton, Sam Coomes, and many others.

Kevin Sampsell is the publisher of Future Tense Books and the author and editor of several books including the memoir, *A Common Pornography*. This essay, Boyfriend, was written in response to Chloe Caldwell's essay, Girlfriend. They performed their "duet" together at the *PANK* reading in Portland in March 2012.

Cheryl and Janet Snell's books include poetry, art, and fiction. Janet's first book of drawings and poetic commentary, *FLYTRAP*, was named a winner in a Cleveland State University Poetry Center competition, and the sisters won the chapbook competition sponsored by Lopside Press for *PRISONER'S DILEMMA*, poems and drawings inspired by game theory. Cheryl has had work in a Sundress Best of the Net, and Janet recently won a COG grant from the Artists of Rubber City. The sisters keep a blog called Scattered Light and collaborate on chapbooks for Scattered Light Library.

Dennis James Sweeney is from Cincinnati but he has spent the last two years working and traveling in Taiwan, southeast Asia, and India. You can find his work elsewhere in *DIAGRAM, dislocate, elimae, Quiddity,* and *TriQuarterly Online*.

Sarah Tourjee probably lives in New England. Her fiction has appeared in *Anomalous Press, Lady Churchill's Rosebud Wristlet, The Sonora Review*, and in at least one other place. She holds an MFA from Brown University.

Jordan Wiklund is a writer and editor from St. Paul in the MFA program at Hamline University. He's working on a manuscript about the history and culture of the game of cribbage and is represented by Dawn Frederick of Red Sofa Literary. He has work forthcoming from *The Believer*.

Kelly A. Wilson grew up in a rural nook of Indianapolis, Indiana, which she still frequents in her poems. Last year, she received an MFA in creative writing and an MA in English literature from Indiana University in Bloomington, IN, and she has been working as a researcher ever since.

PALOOKA

STORIES

POETRY

ESSAYS

PLAYS

GRAPHIC

COMICS

ARTWORK

PHOTOGRAPHY

MULTIMEDIA

WWW.PALOOKAJOURNAL.CO